Black Duck Spring

E. P. DUTTON & CO., INC.
New York 1966

BLACK DUCK SPRING

BRUCE S. WRIGHT

Illustrated by James G. Teason

Other Books by the Author:

High Tide and an East Wind —
the story of the black duck

The Ghost of North America —
the story of the eastern panther

Wildlife Sketches Near and Far

The Monarch of Mularchy Mountain

Introduction and Acknowledgments

This story began with a teen-aged boy following his uncle along the beaches and through the marshes of Château Richer on the St. Lawrence below Quebec. He was carrying a single-barreled 20-gauge shotgun, and their quarry was snipe. The boy looked enviously at the rafts of black ducks lying out in the channel, waiting for dark before coming in to the swamp to feed. It was to be several years before he got one.

The Second World War offered the young man the boy had become the opportunity to spend a summer afloat in the Gulf of St. Lawrence and in Newfoundland waters. With his background as a keen naturalist, a summer as a

5

watch-keeping officer on the bridge of a Canadian corvette hunting U-boats in the Gulf gave him an unrivaled opportunity to study the coastal wildlife of the region. As Executive Officer of the ship, he had at his disposal the personnel and gear of a warship on active service to ensure that nothing of importance was missed—and he decided what was important. He made good use of this unique opportunity.

After the war the story became a master's thesis in Wildlife Management for the late Professor Aldo Leopold at the University of Wisconsin. From there it became the report of the Ducks Unlimited survey of waterfowl in eastern Canada that resulted in the founding of the Northeastern Wildlife Station of the Wildlife Management Institute of Washington, D.C. This station, intended as the eastern counterpart of the Delta Waterfowl Research Station in Manitoba, was established on the campus of the University of New Brunswick in Fredericton, New Brunswick, where it is still in operation.

Men who should be mentioned in the development of this story, and to whom I owe a great debt, are first the late Professor Aldo Leopold; Dr. Ira N. Gabrielson, President of the Wildlife Management Institute, who made possible the Ungava trip and so much more; my assistants who founded the northern banding stations and banded the first ducks in those regions, Alex Reeve at Tinker Harbour in Labrador, E. D. Fowler at Baie Johan Beetz on the North Shore of the Gulf of St. Lawrence, and Denis Benson at Grand Codroy River in Newfoundland. They laid the foundations from which much more was to follow. I was assisted in the studies on the St. John River in New Brunswick by Brian C. Carter, who logged many miles on brood counts and duck surveys.

The winter range was examined from a small private

plane from New Brunswick to Florida. My special thanks are due to its skillful pilot-owner, Dr. John C. Likely of Fredericton.

The interpretation of wildlife events in the region is my own. Where other interpretations are possible and controversy exists, I can state only that I have followed these events closely as a professional wildlife biologist and that the interpretations given are my considered convictions.

BRUCE S. WRIGHT

Fredericton, N.B.
1965

7

Foreword

This is a tale of the wildlife of the northeastern section of our continent that spans the time from the arrival of the Norsemen, about A.D. 1000, to the present. It is woven about the life of a black duck because this hardy bird voyages each year throughout this great region. The females return yearly to a place near their natal marsh, but the males follow whichever female they are mated with that year. Thus, they wander much more widely than the females.

The central figure of this book is a larger and stronger than average male black duck. In the first two sections he makes major journeys into the northland, following his mate of the season. There he experiences all the pleasures and vicissitudes of those remote lands, and meets some of their lesser known inhabitants. In the final section he remains on the winter range along the Atlantic seaboard and in southern Canada, where he encounters a set of greatly different problems. How he acquits himself is typical of his kind.

The work of the men whose job it is to find out the facts about the waterfowl of this region is mentioned. The enthusiasm of youth on his first hunt, where all these men started, is brought out. The fact that almost all the world's most important conservation organizations were founded by men who began their lifelong interest in wildlife with a gun in their hand is not well appreciated. It is a paradox of human nature that the sportsmen who are the greatest threat to the waterfowl are also their most ardent champions. Today the outstanding example of this is the organization called Ducks Unlimited, which raises money from American duck hunters to be spent in Canada to raise more ducks.

This tale tells of black ducks, but it also tells of rare and little-known animals, such as the whale-killing walrus, the newly discovered freshwater seals of Ungava, the gray seals of the Gulf of St. Lawrence, and the white whales that spend their whole lives in this almost landlocked "sea." It relates the story of the seabird rookeries and the sad end of the Labrador duck and the great auk. It tells of the grim slaughter of cormorants for "fun," which still goes on today, and it shows how the last sea mink died.

It recounts the deadly danger to waterfowl and seabirds of oil pollution of the sea, and from spring muskrat trapping inland. Finally, it brings us up to the present with the opening up of the northern breeding grounds, and warns of the grim shadow of pesticide poisons that have already spread from the antarctic ice to the Polar Sea.

Part 1

Chapter One

The young black duck jammed his head hard against the wire. He was angry, wet, and mud-soaked. Through a narrowing funnel he had greedily followed a trail of golden corn to a lavish banquet of the delicious stuff, but there was only one thing wrong—he was not alone.

The duck trap was half full when he squeezed through the funnel and began gobbling up the bait. Other ducks were crowding behind him. Soon the corn was either eaten or tramped into the mud, and he turned to go. Only then did he realize that he was surrounded by a wire fence with a roof over it; and circle as he might, he could not find the entrance. As panic struck them, the ducks leaped into the

15

air and crawled over one another until all were soaked and coated with mud. When the men came in the morning, the black duck was still jabbing his bill into the wire in a futile hunt for some means of escape.

They were herded as gently as possible into the small catching box at one end of the trap, and here a hand reached through an aperture and seized them one by one. He was picked up and held on his back while his sex was determined. An examination of the V-shaped tips of his tail feathers showed that he was not yet a year old. Finally, a numbered metal band was put on his leg and carefully adjusted to be sure it did not constrict the muscles. Through all this, his black button eyes followed every move angrily.

He was in the middle of an assembly line of ducks passing from the trap to the banders. The last biologist to handle him simply sat him on the mud and reached for the next bird. It took him a few seconds to realize he was free, and then he took off with a bound. However, he had forgotten his mud-soaked plumage, and his wings could only carry him about ten yards out onto the pond. There he flopped dismally into the water, and swam for the reeds with all his might. He spent the rest of the day drying out and preening his feathers to remove the mud. As darkness fell he left the pond, never to return.

His first winter would be spent in the maze of sloughs and gullies that stretch for miles along the Jersey shore north of Cape May. The Atlantic rollers beat on the sea-beach, but inside the sand barrier the salt marshes were a haven for wintering ducks, geese, and brant from many parts of the North. As soon as the shooting stopped, he had joined thousands of his kind in this vast maze that had been their winter home for millennia.

As the days began to lengthen, and winter drew to a close, his glands developed and the mating urge glowed in him for the first time. He joined a courting party of males about a pert female, and they displayed before her in heated competition. She watched as they bobbed their heads and chased each other around. Suddenly she leaped into the air and flew a zigzag course over the marshes with her escort of admirers jockeying for position in her train, each vying for the place of honor directly behind her.

The young male, roughly shouldered aside by several full-grown adults, soon found himself bringing up the rear. There was too much competition for him, and he dropped out and returned disconsolate to his pond. However, the urge within him would not be stilled, and he returned again and again to the courting parties. As his gonads developed, he grew bolder and fiercer with other males that approached when he was with a female.

Then one day he found himself first behind the female in courtship flight; she even let him give her tail several strong jerks that pulled out feathers. When she landed, the other males had given up and they were alone. Thus did he win his first mate. From now on, they were inseparable, although he still had to drive off other males who attempted to court her.

Her acceptance of him gave him confidence, and he soon learned he could outfly the others, as well as dominate them on the water. By February all competition for her was over, and he was established as her mate. The red-winged blackbirds cried "Kon-keree!" in approval.

Everywhere she went he followed close behind. One day she rose from the Jersey marshes and headed north. He followed as usual a little above and behind as they flew northward just inside the barrier beach with the ocean swell breaking on the right and the maze of marshes on their left. Canada geese and the smaller brant were feeding on the banks as they passed, and thousands of ducks, all heading north, crowded the bays and gullies.

Ice crystals ringed the pond where they stayed that night, and snow covered the ground; they had wintered south of the permanent snow, but it lay just one day to the north. When they reached Long Island Sound, they joined with other ducks and geese all bound for the far Northeast, and landed amid a raft of purring scaup whose black at both ends and white in the middle silhouette made them conspicuous.

At dusk that evening they rose and flew inland to a spring that was open, then settled gratefully to feed on pondweed and other freshwater foods as a welcome change from the diet of the salt marshes. At dawn they withdrew to an offshore mud bar, where they slept and preened, but before noon they awoke, bestirred themselves, and joined a long string of true sea ducks, eiders and scoters, passing overhead.

They all flew off together toward some islands they could just see away to the northeast; crossing Block Island Sound the islands became clearer. They settled at the first they came to; but because the surf, pounding on an exposed shore, was not to the liking of the blacks, they rose again and pressed on to the next in the chain, where they could see an enclosed tidal lagoon. This was what they were seeking. Here they left the eiders and scoters diving happily just outside the breakers, and settled gladly on the smooth waters of the lagoon.

The island they reached was made world famous by the very creatures they passed over as they came in to land. A mile beyond the breakers the spout of whales rose in the frosty air. Turning to the island of Nantucket, the true sea ducks found miles of sand beaches where they could dive in the surf, and the blacks found the sheltered waters of the lagoon. Both groups were content to stay and rest. Gulls and terns patrolled ceaselessly overhead, eternally on watch for fish or any interesting flotsam. A boy on his daily round of the shore saw the blacks land, and tried to stalk them. They were very alert, however; spying him from a distance, they moved to the other side of the lagoon, and the boy soon gave up the hunt.

The blacks were forced to stay close to the coast, as they were now in a region where all inland waters were solidly frozen at this time of year. Each day as the sun rose higher above the horizon and grew in strength, the urge within the female to reach her natal marsh far to the north grew stronger. Her ardent mate followed wherever she led, knowing not where they were going, and caring less as she chose the route, perfectly content just to be with her.

They had worked to the north end of the lagoon, and one day they rose and joined a large flock of blacks and geese that had arrived from the South. Together they headed out across Nantucket Sound, calling as they went. Veering to the west of Monomoy Point, they crossed the land, and a little over an hour after leaving Nantucket they settled in the great marshes of Cape Cod. Here they met numbers of other waterfowl, all heading in the same direction, and the clatter of their calls could be heard over the distant roar of surf on the outer beaches. The waterfowl of all New England, eastern Canada, and the eastern Arctic were going home, and they were keen to be off.

The next move was across Massachusetts Bay to Plum Island, and as they went north some of the blacks dropped out at each stopping point. They had reached their breed-

19

ing grounds, and would go no farther. They settled in the local marshes to await the breakup of inland waters.

Ahead lay the northern coast, starting with the long sand beaches leading into the jagged indentations of the eastern Maine shore at the entrance to the Bay of Fundy. As the host moved northward, it picked up pockets of birds that had wintered in these higher latitudes. These groups had already sent scouts inland looking for open water, and as soon as any was found a pair or two of blacks and some black-and-white goldeneyes would move in and take possession. The gaudy goldeneye drakes, in courting parties of six or seven with one or two brownish females, called "Speer, speer," and the females answered with a sharp "Cur-r-rew."

They loafed for a week amid the many islands and shoals of Penobscot Bay, and then moved again. The next stop was the great tidal estuary of Passamaquoddy Bay, where they circled over the rushing tides forming whirlpools between the islands as those seagoing shorebirds the phalaropes danced like sea sprites from one long line of drifting seaweed to the next. Small porpoises plunged madly through the vortex of the main whirlpool, and a piked whale blew sonorously as he too made use of this natural centrifuge that concentrated his food.

That night the pair were resting on a weed-covered rock with the ebbing tide swirling past a few feet below. Suddenly the male's head shot up and he uttered a loud warning squawk. A glistening head with large eyes broke the surface a few feet in front and surveyed them inquisitively. After sharply inhaling, it sank with hardly a ripple, and did not reappear. Gradually the ducks settled down to their sleep as the harbor seal went back to his fishing.

At dawn next day a lone bald eagle soared in great

sweeps low over the shoals. His natural food was dead fish, but he had wintered in the North that year, and it had been a grim one. Late in the season, when the freezing shore had covered most of his hunting areas with ice, he found a group of ducks trapped in an ice-rimmed pool with their food almost gone. Their movements kept the pool open, and as they weakened they were more and more loath to leave it. When he found the ducks he had eaten only one small dead fish in the past two days, and he was very hungry.

Never before had he considered ducks as food because they were too hard to catch. But now he was desperate. To his own surprise he caught a half-starved duck on his first pass. He flew off exultantly to a nearby stub to eat it. When breakup came there were no more ducks in the pool, and the eagle had become a confirmed duck killer.

Now, soaring over the ledges, he saw scores upon scores of ducks, geese, and brant packed in dark lines on each. Disregarding the smaller ducks, he dived like a thunder-bolt upon a group of geese wading in a tide pool. Their slow running takeoff was no match for his plunging speed, and he set his talons firmly in the back of a goose. Never before had he seized such large prey, and there was no chance of taking off with it. He dragged it to the side of the pool and there began his meal. The feathers that he plucked from the carcass drifted along the shore toward the pair of blacks on a nearby ledge, causing them to shift uneasily.

Chapter Two

When the pair reached the head of the Bay of Fundy, they flew across the narrow isthmus of land to Northumberland Strait and the Gulf of St. Lawrence. There they entered a world where spring had barely begun. They pressed on to the red shores of Prince Edward Island and settled in the salt marshes behind the endless beaches of the north coast. There they stayed until the last of the harp seal pups had left the rotting ice out in the Gulf, and the seabirds had streamed off to their rookeries at Cape St. Mary's on the coast of Newfoundland, Percé Rock on the Gaspé coast, and the Bird Rocks north of that maze of sandbars in the middle of the Gulf called the Magdalen Islands.

Here the frenzied activities of the breeding season began, but still the blacks must wait for the ice of the last area of the region to break up—Labrador.

Their ancestors had landed on these beaches two hundred years before to hear the roaring of the walrus hauled out on the sands. The scene then was one of great numbers of wild creatures in a virgin land: hordes of sandpipers, curlews, plovers, and other shorebirds thronged the miles of beach, dashing back and forth just ahead of the breaking waves, and the great walruses lay piled in heaps of snoring flesh in the shallow water and far up on the sand. Periodically these heaps erupted as a pair of tusks flashed in the sun and gave its neighbor a savage dig. Brant, geese, and sea ducks swam offshore. Still farther out were those colony-nesters of the sea cliffs, the murres and puffins. Dovekies, the smallest of the auks, a starling-sized miniature of the great auk but with serviceable wings, Labrador ducks, and great auks were the farthest out of all. Overhead wheeled delicate terns, gulls, and the beautiful goose-sized gannets that swept effortlessly about on their long wings searching for fish. When they found a school a whole flock would fold their wings and dive like plummets from fifty feet or more in the air. They sent up a splash quite four feet high as they knifed through the surface and plunged deep into the sea after their quarry. When they finished their fishing, they all flew off up the coast. They were returning to their nesting colonies on Bonaventure Island and Percé Rock on the Gaspé coast, the Bird Rocks, or Cape St. Mary's in Newfoundland where they would cover the islands like snow and defend their nests with their long, powerful beaks in the orderly life of the great rookery.

Just behind the beaches stretched miles of brackish

The northern journeys described in Parts I and II

HUDSON
BAY

Cape Jones

Twin Islands

Seal Lakes

Akpotok
Island

False River

Nest

NEWFOUNDLAND

Tinker
Harbour

Goose Bay

Nest

LABRADOR

Black
Duck
Brook

Q U E B E C

Baise Johan-Beetz

Seven
Islands Bay

JACQUES   CARTIER PASSAGE

ANTICOSTI
ISLAND

GASPE
PASSAGE

GULF OF
ST. LAWRENCE

Grand
Codroy
River

ST. LAWRENCE RIVER

Cap Tourmente

QUEBEC

MONTREAL

OTTAWA

Lake Champlain

NEW
BRUNSWICK

Jemseg

MAINE

Tabusintas

PRINCE
EDWARD
ISLAND

MAGDALEN
ISLANDS

CABOT STRAIT

CAPE BRETON
ISLAND

Tantramar

BAY OF FUNDY   Yarmouth

ATLANTIC OCEAN

ponds and inlets where puddle ducks and still more geese were everywhere. Snipe pattered through the wet meadows and swooped like nighthawks overhead, with their wings and tails making a humming sound called "winnowing." At dawn and dusk a male woodcock, from the edge of the alders, emitted at regular intervals a sound like a nasal electric buzzer that ornithologists call his "peent," and carried on his spiral flight song to his silent mate crouching on the russet leaves. Here was a natural home for the black ducks; paired birds flew up every stream and inlet to nest. The walrus were gone now, as were the Labrador ducks and the great auks, but the beaches and the ponds and inlets were still there.

Then one day the natural clock that was in her told the female it was time to press on again to the North. They flew from Prince Edward Island across the open sea to the Magdalens and, after a short rest, on to the shores of Newfoundland. Turning north, they followed the jagged coast, with the Long Range Mountains looming on their right, for three hundred miles to the tip of the great northern peninsula. Here again they settled to rest.

The spot they chose was well known to all of their kind coming and going to the vast Labrador country to the north.

It was the mouth of a small brook running into Épaves Bay on the south shore of the Strait of Belle Isle. As they set their tired wings and slanted down, the island with its famous light in the entrance to the Strait and the other islands in the bay stood out clearly in the setting sun against the dark loom of the Labrador coast beyond. They had reached Black Duck Brook where some say once stood Straumfjord, the settlement of the Viking Karlstefni in Vinland. If this be so—and carbon-14 dating of artifacts shows that Iron Age man lived there about A.D. 1000, the date of his voyage—then here at this time Snorri, son of Karlstefni, the first white child born in North America, heard the calling of black ducks who gave their name to the brook running past the sod and stone house where he was born. The long association of white men and black ducks had begun.

After a wait of a few days to rest and recuperate, the pair crossed the Strait and followed the Labrador coast north. For two hundred miles they crossed rugged promontories and deep bays. They passed a forty-mile-long white-sand beach that some say was the strand of the Vikings; but this was not to her liking, and the female bored steadily ahead until finally she came to a great inlet that closed to a narrow gut with strong rushing tides. She passed over the post at its mouth and pressed on inland as far as there was any open water, and here they set their wings and glided down to land on the shores of Lake Melville, the great tidal lake that stretches for a hundred miles into the interior of southern Labrador. The young female was home at last, and the male looked around him curiously at the strange landscape.

The paired blacks settled on the south shore of Lake Melville, which had as a background the rolling summits of the Mealy Mountains just emerging from the winter snow. For some days they loafed and rested along the shore, regaining their strength after their fifteen-hundred-mile journey from Cape May. As soon as brown patches of open ground began to show on the slopes of the mountains, they flew daily to timberline and fed happily on the blueberries that had remained on the bushes all winter under the snow. Here for the last time that season they encountered man.

A boatload of men and boys left the settlement of North West River on the north shore of Lake Melville and landed close to the pair. The ducks prudently withdrew into the purple haze of alders along the shore as the boat passed, and were unnoticed. The party spent the day working their way through the spruce and scrub on the lower slopes, and camped for the night at timberline. At dawn next day they were up and carefully scanning the open patches of blueberry barrens that dotted the slopes above. They had not long to wait; the clangor of goose talk soon reached their ears, and a flock of twenty Canadas sailed in on set wings to land two hundred yards away. They were followed by a pair of black ducks.

"Give 'em half an hour to sittle down, b'ys," said the leader.

After the interval they spread out and began to stalk the feeding geese, whose wily sentinel had relaxed, lowered his head, and begun feeding. Soon the guns were within range.

"Now, b'ys!" called the leader, and a volley cut into the feeding flock. Ten birds died instantly, and two more were cut down as they tried to drag themselves to cover. The remainder took off screaming the now unnecessary alarm, and the roar of gunfire bounded along the silent mountains. The blacks had been out of the line of fire and made good their escape while the triumphant hunters were reloading. They were not to see man again until fall.

Back at the village, the women laughed at their purple-stained hands after cleaning the blueberry-filled geese; the tough, stringy meat was looked upon as a great delicacy after the lean rations of late winter.

Spring had come to Lake Melville.

As soon as the last ice disappeared from the muskeg ponds, the female began searching for a nest site. She settled on a small pond, fringed with sedge, well out in a muskeg. Nearby was a stunted black spruce with the lowest tier of its branches lying on the ground. She crawled onto them and made a hollow in the accumulation of dry needles, lining it with down from her breast as the eggs came one by one until she had a clutch of nine. Her days were now spent incubating; whenever she left the nest she carefully covered the eggs with down to make them almost invisible. Her mate had taken up a loafing spot in the pond, and she joined him morning and evening to feed. The rest of his time he spent loafing and preening on an old log that jutted from the pond, or sleeping away the lengthening days.

As the spring runoff came to an end, the water level in the pond dropped, and the channel connecting it with the other waterways of the muskeg dried up. All aquatic life was now isolated where it was until fall, and among it was a two-foot northern pike. He lived on water beetles, frogs, and salamanders, as well as upon the smaller fish. The only occupants of the pond larger than himself were the pair of black ducks, who lived their normal lives completely oblivious of his presence.

On June 5th the first egg hatched. Soon the rest of the brood was completed, and they dried quickly in the bright sun. It was only a few feet through the matted vegetation to the water's edge, and the female moved through it slowly, murmuring softly to the chicks struggling through the tangle behind. At the edge she slipped in quietly. The tired ducklings flopped onto the smooth surface one by one as they emerged from the brush. When they were all present she led them to a shallow cove where they were soon feeding on mosquito larvae.

The pike lay in his usual lurking spot in the shadow of a log on the far side of the pond. He had heard the ducks enter the water, and he had also heard the stream of little plops that marked the arrival of the ducklings; but as they were new sounds to him, and obviously associated with the ducks, he paid no attention. An hour later the duck and her brood had fed around the margin. The pike's log lay directly ahead of them. She swam slowly around the end of it, followed by the ducklings in a group—all but one, which had strayed several yards behind. As the other ducklings passed out of sight around the log, it put on a spurt to catch up.

The pike watched warily as the duck approached his hiding place. As she passed and the ducklings came into view, his excitement mounted. It reached fever pitch as the tail of the brood passed over him, but as he had never seen this before their mass gave him pause, and he did not strike. Then from the rear came a lone duckling paddling frantically along the surface with wings and feet, in obvious panic at being left behind. This was too much for any pike to resist—with a flick of his tail he struck, and the duckling disappeared in a swirl of water. The duck paddled on, followed by the rest of her brood, quite unaware of the sudden end of the short life of one of her family.

From then on the pike followed the brood wherever it went. He could never gather the courage to attack when the ducklings were together, but stragglers disappeared one by one. By the time they were two weeks old, the brood was reduced to four, and it seemed certain that none would reach flying age. The annual reproduction of the pair, for which they had crossed over a thousand miles of strange lands and stormy seas, seemed doomed.

Then one day the pike was lying at the surface, only a few feet from the ducklings bunched behind the female. He was hungry, and making ready for his next attack as soon as a duckling strayed. Suddenly the female looked up, uttered the alarm, and she and the ducklings raced for the cover of the vegetation as a ripping sound was heard overhead. An osprey plunged like a dropping stone into the water a few feet from where they had been, and with a great struggle of flapping wings it emerged with the pike fast in its talons. Flying low across the water, it just managed to clear the vegetation on the far shore as it became airborne. The pike thrashed and snapped and sent a silver spray in all directions, but the relentless grip never relaxed; the fish was seen no more in the pond.

In due course the four ducklings took wing and joined the thousands of their generation wandering about the rivers and lakes, bays and inlets of Labrador. The female, her duties for the season over, gratefully retired into the remotest part of the muskeg to molt. As the rest of the summer slid by, the ducklings gathered in bunches excitedly trying out this wonderful new ability that had come to them—the power of flight. At first they worked at it frantically, their young wings beating twice as fast as the powerful strokes of the older birds. Practicing banking and sideslipping, they wandered from their natal marsh for the first time in their lives.

When the incubation period had drawn to a close, the male deserted his mate and left the muskeg pool to join other males who were gathering out on Lake Melville to molt. They shed their feathers gradually. The long primaries of their wings, which had borne them over a

thousand miles since they grew the previous summer, were now worn and loose, and fell out one by one. Soon they were flightless, and had to resort to diving to escape their enemies. They became very alert, staying well out in open water, swimming in only to feed in the shallows after dark. For almost two weeks they lived like this, and then their new flight feathers began to appear. Soon they were trying them out in aerial gymnastics over the lake. Quickly they regained their former brilliant mastery of the air.

As soon as he could fly again, the male moved out to the coast. He was attracted to a great tide flat by the sound of other ducks and geese. Although he saw a fishing boat anchored in a nearby cove, he was reassured by the numbers of waterfowl behaving unconcernedly nearby. He joined the multitude happily and was soon lost among a thousand of his kind.

At dusk that night the tide was high. The ducks swam to the water's edge to feed. The black and a group of others followed an inlet when he discovered a few grains of delicious corn—such as he had not tasted since the disastrous day he found himself in the trap and men had put the band on his leg. He swam around a bend, and there in front of him on a mud bar stood one of those round wire traps with golden corn strewn enticingly at the entrance to the funnel, and much more inside. He watched cautiously from a distance as several greedy youngsters rushed in, forced their way up the funnel, and fell on the banquet awaiting within. A pintail with her complete brood not yet awing followed them into the trap, but he rose and flew back to the beach, for his inborn caution would not let him make that mistake twice.

At first light the next morning a biologist left the fishing boat and rowed off to make the rounds of his duck traps. He was banding the first ducks ever banded in Labrador, and when he came to the brood of pintails he was particularly delighted to see they could not fly. They must have been hatched within swimming distance of the trap, and he would have an exact record of their point of origin if they were subsequently shot. That fall he stayed and banded at Tinker Harbour on the Labrador coast until the autumn gales drove both him and the waterfowl to seek a more southerly climate. He returned to his headquarters far to the south, and the ducks and geese began the fall migration.

Chapter Three

The concentration of waterfowl at Tinker Harbour grew as bad weather forced all the birds from Ungava Bay and the northern coast south. There was no massed movement as groups of birds leapfrogged each other to find a favorable spot with plenty of food where they stayed until the southward-creeping frost drove them out.

The survivors of the brood hatched at the muskeg pond stayed together until they reached Tinker Harbour. There they broke up, each going his own way with whatever group it happened to be at the time. Two of the young ducks joined a mixed group of blacks and green-winged teal that dropped south to the Strait of Belle Isle and crossed to Newfoundland. Instead of following the west coast south, as had the pair coming north, they followed the east coast of the northern peninsula into White Bay and up the rivers inland to the large lakes of western Newfoundland.

Here they were in the country of the great moose eruption. Moose from New Brunswick had been introduced by the Newfoundland authorities to this land, where they found themselves so completely at home, and with no competition, that they increased prodigiously, becoming a menace to the regeneration of the forest upon which the great pulp and paper industry of Newfoundland depends. The ducks saw many of these huge creatures about the lakes and swales where they stopped to feed. Each evening the long-drawn-out call of the cows echoed across the silent lakes. The answering grunt of the great bulls, thrashing their way through the spruces and alders to the rendezvous, startled the sleeping ducks.

One frosty morning they were sitting on some boulders beside a lake with their heads under their wings when they were startled by a strange clicking sound coming from the heavy black spruces behind them. A band of caribou stepped cautiously into the open, and the clicking sound, caused by their hooves, stopped as they stood and stared. Two stags immediately began sparring, but the does paid no attention to them and wandered down to the lake to drink.

The young ducks withdrew discreetly before them into the lake and stared as these strange creatures splashed along the shallows. The young fawns waded out into the lake, extending soft muzzles to sniff at the ducks, who kept demurely just out of reach. A sort of game developed between them. The fawns skipped and pranced along the shore while the placid does, chewing their cuds, watched indifferently.

In this land of the moose and the caribou, few people bothered to molest the ducks on the inland lakes. One evening, when they were feeding at dusk in the shallows, a great horned owl appeared from nowhere and picked up one of the young blacks, which died instantly in the vise-like grip that drove the long, sharp talons completely through its body. The others raced for the shelter of vegetation on shore.

Their movement caught the keen eyes of a hunting lynx, and he lay down on a log to watch. He was almost invisible in the deep shadows, as the gray moss on the stunted spruces matched his coat perfectly. He remained silently watching until the ducks, after the panic of the owl's attack had subsided, cautiously returned to the water and resumed feeding. The following night he arrived at the lake shore early and unseen, and took up his position directly opposite the ducks, as close to the water as he could find cover.

As the shadows lengthened and darkness gathered, the ducks fed in the shallows only a few yards from the gray form stretched motionless beside the log. But this time an old female black duck was more alert. Her head was up, her keen eyes watching when the owl launched its attack from the spruces. As it broke into the clear, falling like a feathered bomb toward the ducks, she uttered the alarm, and each duck dived headlong into the tangle. The owl was thwarted, but one young duck came to rest almost between the forepaws of the lynx, who seized it with one flick of a claw-lined paw.

Thus they wandered through the lake country of western Newfoundland, on to its southwest corner. Here they

entered the Codroy Valley and found the best marshes
they had encountered so far. At this concentration point
for the freshwater ducks of the island, they joined the
others in an orgy of feeding and playing before leaving
for the mainland to make their first acquaintance with
heavy shooting.

Meanwhile, back at Tinker Harbour, the male had
joined a group that set out in a different direction. They

crossed the eastern tip of the Mealy Mountains and dropped into the great muskegs at the head of the Eagle and Paradise rivers, where they fed avidly on the bog cranberries that were all about. They moved overland in a southerly direction and came out on the shore of the Gulf of St. Lawrence well to the west of the Strait of Belle Isle. This bleak, rocky coast was the home of many sea ducks, murres, razor-billed auks, and cormorants, and the blacks flew inland to fresh water each night to feed.

As they followed this shore westward for over two hundred miles, past the mouths of innumerable rivers where men netted both salmon and seals, they retained their daily pattern of resting on the salt water and feeding on the fresh wherever the shore allowed.

For five hundred years after the bearded Vikings abandoned Straumfjord at Black Duck Brook in northern Newfoundland to sail back to Greenland with the boy Snorri, the world of the black ducks did not know Europeans. Then one day an Indian lounged before his skin tent on the north shore of the Gulf of St. Lawrence, watching his squaw scraping a sealskin. Lying downwind of his fire so the smoke would keep off the flies, he enjoyed his leisure. He had spent the long hard winter hunting in the interior, and this was his season to rest. His eyes wandered down to the edge of the seashore and strayed out over the gray waters. Suddenly he came to attention. He sprang to his feet, shouting and pointing as a ship under full sail rounded the point and headed into his bay. The white man had come to the almost landlocked sea we call the Gulf of St. Lawrence for the first time. The year was 1533. Two of the Indian's children were out in the bay hunting ducks with their bird darts when the ship came in sight. Several ducks lay in the bottom of their canoe. They were so struck with astonishment and fear as the great ship bore down on them that they made no attempt to escape as a boathook brought them alongside. They were taken before the captain, Jacques Cartier, who made every effort to communicate with them. Finally they were made to understand that he came in peace and wanted to go ashore and make friends with their people. They were returned to their canoe loaded with presents. As they cast off, the elder boy looked up at the row of grinning seamen lining the rail and tossed up to them one of the ducks from the bottom of the canoe. It was all he had to offer in return for the many strange and beautiful gifts they had given him. Then they pulled for the shore with all their might.

That night Captain Cartier dined on black duck, the first eaten by a European since the days of the Norsemen. He found it tough, as it had been killed that day, but excellent by the standards of ship's provisions, and it went very well with the rich red wine of France.

Captain Cartier sailed along the north shore of the Gulf of St. Lawrence and Gaspé where he saw the great throngs of black ducks and geese, eiders, scoters, and Labrador ducks amid myriads of seabirds. He marveled at what he saw, made friends with the Indians, took possession of the land in the name of the King of France, and sailed away. For two hundred years afterward, man had no effect upon the feathered host. As the females returned year after year to their natal place to produce their young, the continuity that builds a flyway went unbroken. The white man had come to the land of the red, but so far he had made no impression upon the wildlife.

The sea mammals were the first to feel the weight of his iron as the Basque whalers pushed up the St. Lawrence, setting up their tryworks on the islands for extracting the oil from these animals. The pothead whales followed the capelin, a small fish of the smelt family, and the northern equivalent of the menhaden that abounded farther south along the Atlantic coast, into the bays of Newfoundland in great schools, and the harp, or saddleback, seals bred on the pack ice far out in the Gulf. The white whales, a completely isolated population, spent their whole lives in the Gulf, but to these the whalers paid scant attention. The great whales were their prey, and they were there in plenty. Over all, long strings of black ducks came and went each season like dark voyagers bound for a hidden land.

Now the white man was entering the black duck's world at several points. The settlement of Captain John Smith at Jamestown, Virginia, saw black ducks for most of the year, and the colonists were quick to discover how excellent they tasted. Two years after the settlement of the Virginia colony, Henry Hudson sailed past Long Island through the very heart of a black-duck concentration area to discover a smaller island the Indians considered unimportant. They called the place Manhattan, and gladly bartered it away seventeen years later for some of the strangers' goods.

The danger that man presented to the animal world was brought forcibly to the attention of the opening meeting of the Legislature of Prince Edward Island. This august body, composed of the "eighteen inhabitants who could make a tolerable appearance in the House," passed as their first act of business a regulation requiring a license for "fishing seacows." The walruses that thronged the beaches and devoured the delicious oysters by the ton when the first settlers arrived were being rapidly exterminated.

Though the well-intentioned act was passed, it could not be enforced, and the killing continued unabated. Within

41

a few years the last survivors had fled to the north, but even today occasional stragglers enter the Gulf through Belle Isle Strait and wander about their old haunts. A lone bull was killed on the Nova Scotia side of the entrance to the Bay of Fundy, far to the south, in 1937. These huge creatures, reported to weigh as much as two tons at Prince Edward Island, so fierce in the water but so dull and helpless against men with guns on land, were doomed by their valuable beef, hides, oil, and ivory. The first species of the fauna that Captain Cartier saw had been decimated.

The great auks had also vanished from the Gulf, where not long before they had fished around the Bird Rocks and had seen the Labrador ducks on every sand shoal of the Magdalens. Some of them had landed on the outermost of the Bird Rocks, where their neat black-and-white patterns were clearly visible as they stood on the ledges just above the surf. They were the largest birds on the lower rocks, outstripped in size only by the gannets of the higher ground.

In strange contrast to their puny wings were their tremendously powerful feet and legs, which drove them through three thousand miles of stormy seas from their breeding grounds in the remote North Atlantic islands to their wintering grounds off the Carolina coasts and back each year. Their wings were used as stabilizers and for propulsion underwater, but they were quite incapable of lifting their heavy bodies into the air. The great auks stayed together in a group even among the teeming thousands of other birds at the rookery, and a warning snap from the powerful beak discouraged any intimacy from outsiders.

At this time a great advance in seamanship had been made, and with it a genius for exploration had developed among the peoples of northern Europe. Soon all the off-shore islands in the North Atlantic had been discovered, and the breeding places of the seabirds were laid open to the local fishermen.

Those of Newfoundland soon found the only known breeding colony of great auks on their shore at Funk Island off the northeast coast. They established camps there during the breeding season for the sole purpose of killing the birds as each female waddled ashore to produce her solitary egg. A great cod fishery had been found on the shores of Labrador, and fleets of schooners went north each spring to spend the summer fishing "down north on the Labrador." On passage they called at Funk Island to stock up with great auks and other seabirds for eggs and down, food and bait.

The helpless great auks could even be made to walk the plank to their death, filling the waiting boats with a mini-mum of effort. A boat would be secured alongside a rock and a plank laid from the shore to the gunwale. The land party would then surround a group of birds and herd them slowly toward the boat, with a man on either side of the plank to prevent them reaching the water. They followed in dumb procession across the plank and into the boat, where they were clubbed to death and neatly stowed so that each load contained the largest possible number.

At the shore camps they were killed and skinned with a single jerk. Their oily bodies served as fuel for the fires to boil those to be kept as food. Of all birds, they were the most eagerly sought because they caused the fishermen the least effort in obtaining a cargo of food, bait, eggs, and feathers. A few thinking men realized what was happening and raised their voices in protest, but they were far away and powerless to do anything about the slaughter.

Each year the great auks became fewer and fewer about their old winter haunts from Nova Scotia to the Carolinas, and by 1840 they were almost all gone. The end came on June 3, 1844. On this day the last pair of great auks sat on a shelf of the cliff of Eldey Rock off the southwest coast of Iceland. Their thick-shelled egg, with its pointed end so that it would roll in circles but would not fall off a ledge, lay between the female's horny feet. In the bay below, a sturdy three-master dropped anchor and put over a boat. Six men and three boys came ashore.

The helpless murres in their crowded colony below were unable to take off from level ground, and the men came among them swinging their clubs. As they hacked their way through the nesting birds, leaving a path of dead and dying in their wake, the boys followed behind, gathering the eggs. One of the men stopped to wipe the sweat from his eyes, and glanced up at the cliff.

"Garefowl!" he shouted, pointing excitedly to the two great birds looking down on the ghastly scene below.

At once the men spread out and blocked the birds' path to the water. The auks stayed with their lone egg to the last minute and then made a dash for the sea. But it was hopeless from the moment they were seen, and the falling clubs ended the lives of the last pair of great auks. For good measure the boys tramped on the strange egg. The "penguin" of the North Atlantic had, entirely at the hands of man, come to the end of its long stay on earth. A few scientists noted their passing with regret, but the only ones really affected were the fishermen, who now would have to work harder for their supplies. The islands were still teeming with birds, but all were able to fly.

The black ducks, who met the great auks each year during migration and on the winter range, saw only open water when they looked to seaward now—and so it has been ever since. The first of the bird life of the Atlantic seaboard as it was discovered by white men had disappeared.

Chapter Four

Thirteen years after the last walrus disappeared from the beaches of Prince Edward Island, the scientific world got its first word of something new to be found along the northeast coast of North America. In 1788 a scientist published the first description of a new sea duck from the Atlantic coast. He called it *Anas labradoria,* the Labrador duck. Later the name was changed to *Camptorhynchus labradorium* (Gmelin), and as such it is known today. It was a medium-sized, smart-appearing bird that was usually found along sandy bays and beaches where it dived for shellfish just outside the breakers with the eiders, scoters, and old squaws. It was known as the "sand shoal duck" by the coast dwellers, and in winter it could be found from Nova Scotia to Chesapeake Bay, although a few stragglers wandered up the St. Lawrence. A sea duck, it was nevertheless closely associated with the wintering black ducks of the region.

No one ever found their breeding range, but it is thought to have been on the coastal islands of the north shore of the Gulf of St. Lawrence and in southern Labrador. The male was a gaudy black-and-white bird with a snow-white head and neck with a black stripe down the crown and a black necklace around the throat. The wing coverts were also white, but all the rest of the bird was black. The females were much less showy and were mostly brownish-gray.

They were just another sea duck to the market gunners who supplied waterfowl to the markets of the rising cities along the Atlantic seaboard, and because they were fishy they were not in great demand. No one paid them much attention, and they mingled with the migrating and wintering black ducks all along the coast from the mid-Atlantic states to the north shore of the Gulf.

When they flew, their wings gave off a whistling sound like those of the goldeneye, or whistler. They usually traveled in groups of seven to ten together. Shy, and harder to approach than most sea ducks, they found the habits of the coastwise blacks much to their liking. Their flight was swift and sure, and they had no trouble in keeping up with their dark neighbors. They competed with them in no important way, although when the blacks were on their marine habitat they ate some of the small crustaceans that were the main food of the Labrador ducks. The blacks were freshwater ducks who wintered on the sea, but the Labradors were bound the year round to salt water. This distinction was to stand the blacks in good stead in the near future.

The world's population of Labrador ducks entered the Gulf of St. Lawrence each spring either through Cabot Strait or overland from the Bay of Fundy. When they reached the north shore, they nested on the coastal islands amid the teeming seabirds and the eiders and scoters. They were so few in number that they were lost in the multitude of other birds, and no nest of theirs was ever definitely located.

One day many years ago a fishing schooner lay off one of these islands. The crew had been hauling in cod as fast as they could get their hooks in the water, and the ship was nearly full. The time had almost come to leave. When the weary crew had finished its task, eaten a frugal meal, and rested, one of them approached the captain. He asked permission to take a boat over to one of the nearby islands to search for birds' eggs to provide a fresh meal for the crew. The captain granted his request but warned him to return at once if the wind changed. Soon he and his mate were under way.

When they landed they were greeted by a roar of wings; the air was filled with frightened birds. The din assaulted their eardrums, but there were eggs everywhere, and soon they had filled every container they possessed. To these hungry fishermen an egg was an egg, and they made no conscious selection. They made three trips that day, bringing all they could carry each time, and on the last trip a boy on his first voyage collected some brownish down he found among the tussocks, and stuffed it inside his shirt. It would be a present for his mother when he got home, as she was always saving down from ducks for the family pillows. This was finer down than he had ever seen.

From then on, whenever the captain took his schooner to the north shore he made a practice of filling up with eggs before starting home. The boy's mother marveled at the excellence of the down he brought home and told him to bring back more—much more—the next season.

Thus were born the twin practices of egging and down hunting. Soon schooners were going to the bird islands with no other object than a cargo of eggs and down. As the practice grew, the coastal nesting species were devastated, but the inland nesting black ducks were unaffected. The eggers soon learned that the best way to ensure the freshness of their cargo was to go through the rookery and smash every egg they could find. A week later they would return and fill up with fresh ones laid since their last visit. No species could suffer this drain indefinitely, and soon the decline set in.

As the birds decreased, keen competition developed among the hunters for the best places, and in the end pitched battles were fought between fishermen legitimately in search of provisions and the eggers who wished to keep the rookeries for themselves. Fist and club, knife and shotgun were all called into play, but the fishermen usually prevailed through weight of numbers. After the battle they would raid the eggers' shallop, destroying the cargo and leaving them to begin all over again. In a few years the swirling clouds of birds were so reduced that these raids were no longer profitable, and the trade died out, ruined by its own greed.

Then one day in the spring of 1833 a sail appeared off the Bird Rocks in the Gulf. It was the ship *Ripley,* and it bore the most famous ornithologist of his day—John James Audubon. He was on his way to visit the bird colonies along the north shore (which he called Labrador).

There he saw, and was the first to describe, the ruthless slaughter of the breeding birds by the eggers and down hunters. The type of ruffian engaged in the trade appalled him, and he recorded his impressions vividly for posterity. To him we owe the first description of the dreadful slaughter of the seabirds along the coast which provides a clue to the disappearance of the Labrador duck.

Thirty years after the eggers and down hunters had put themselves out of business, the seabird colonies began to recover—but not so the Labrador duck. No one ever saw this duck on its nest, and the best guess still is that it nested on the coastal islands of the north shore and southern Labrador. It was unknown farther north in Labrador and apparently never reached Greenland, and the only known eggs were in a museum in Dresden, Germany, labeled simply "from Labrador." If they survived the bombing of the Second World War, they have disappeared behind the iron curtain.

The gaudy black-and-white drakes were the first to go. It was suggested, but never proved, that this was because the males did not reach maturity until their second year, and with the increased hunting fewer and fewer reached that age. This seems unlikely, as other species, much more heavily hunted because of their superior table qualities, were not having this trouble. The Labradors lived with the other sea ducks, and fed by diving in the surf for small shellfish. There was never any evidence of a food shortage, and the eiders, scoters, and old squaws, their closest associates, slowly recovered from the effects of the raiders, while the Labradors gradually faded out. It may have been that, unlike the others, who had a widely scattered breeding range along hundreds of miles of coastline, the Labrador ducks were restricted by some unknown factor to a much more limited area and that the raiders pushed them beyond the point of no return, but even this is conjecture.

The full story will never be known. All we know is that each spring they disappeared to the north with the others, and each fall fewer and fewer came south. They were now almost totally unmolested by man on their breeding ground, but they never recovered. In 1871 the last specimen was taken at Grand Manan Island in New Brunswick, and four years later a female was shot near Long Island. On December 12, 1878, a specimen was shot by a boy at Elmira, New York, and since then no one has seen a Labrador duck. Another species of the wildlife of the region had disappeared from this earth. They were never shot in anything like the numbers that other, more desirable, species were, and there is no natural factor that can be blamed for their extinction. They lived on the sea, the most stable of all habitats, and their environment has not changed. Something changed, however, but we shall never know what.

Meanwhile, toward the end, a man went out on the Barnegat beaches and set a trotline in one of the bays. He baited the hooks with small mussels and clams, and laid them out over the sandbars. When he returned the next morning to haul his line, he felt the weight on it and knew he had made a catch. Slowly and deliberately he hauled in and removed the fish on the hooks nearest shore. As he came to the end his eyes widened with surprise. On the last two hooks were a drake Labrador duck in full plumage and his brownish mate with the white stripe behind her eyes. They were both drowned, but so rare had they become that the man did not know what manner of ducks they were. He took them home and sold the drake to a collector, and that night they ate the female for dinner.

For the rest of his life he remembered the day he caught the "black belly" on the trotline. He never again saw another.

Moving westward along the coast, the male black reached the small fishing village of Baie Johan Beetz on the north shore, opposite the center of Anticosti Island. Here he heard occasional shots, and he remembered from the previous fall what they meant. A small river ran into the sea from a lake about two miles inland at the foot of the escarpment. This lake was a favorite rendezvous and feeding ground for the freshwater ducks migrating along the coast; and the biologist, studying the routes the birds from this vast region took to and from their breeding grounds, duly noted it and established a banding station there.

The first night the male black visited the lake with a number of other migrants, he noticed some green-winged teal flying up a stream flowing into the lake, and he followed out of curiosity. At the first bend he found a few grains of corn on a mudbank, and gobbled them up greedily, although a dim warning bell seemed to be ringing somewhere inside him. Around the next bend he found the reason: on a mud bar sticking out into the brook stood one of those circular wire duck traps he had experienced before, and a struggling mass of blacks and teal were fighting for the pile of golden corn that was the bait. Knowing full well what this meant, he leaped into the air and returned to the lake.

Henceforth he stayed well away from the trap, remaining discreetly under cover when the men came each morning to clean it and band the night's catch. The banding station was in full operation now, as the migration was at its peak and each night the traps were full.

As the season advanced, birds from the north came through, and numbers of green-winged teal used the lake. The banders caught them each night. Some soon learned that they were not injured by being handled, and came back night after night to feed on the bait. Soon these "freeloaders" became such a nuisance that the banders handled them with scant ceremony.

A duck hawk found the flights of teal using the lake. One day, as the big male black sat on his boulder watching, a skein of teal crossed the lake. The hawk, swooping in on them, struck one in a shower of feathers. The teal dropped like a stone into the lake, but as it was not dead, it dived at once. The hawk circled above for a moment and then turned in pursuit of the fleeing flock. Although frightened teal are among the fastest of fliers, it overtook them in horizontal flight in a matter of minutes. This time the bird it struck was dead when it hit the ground. The graceful predator landed beside it and began its meal.

The squabbling and flapping of the ducks in the traps could be heard a considerable distance over the silent lake. One night two large yellow eyes swung around and two sharp ear tufts lifted as the noise reached them up on the escarpment beyond. In utter silence a great horned owl launched itself from a stub and glided over the lake. It saw a struggling mass of ducks in the trap; fascinated, it dropped to watch from a nearby tree. Soon it realized the ducks could not leave the spot, and it dived directly at the center of the milling mass with talons extended, but the netting that formed the roof brought it up short while the terrified ducks cowered below. Frustrated, the owl returned to the tree to watch.

The next night, when the ducks arrived from the sea to follow the trail of corn into the trap, the owl saw them

enter the funnel and push their way through, busily gobbling as they went. When the last black had wormed its
way in, and the frantic flying against the wire had begun,
the great owl left its perch and floated as lightly as a
feather to the entrance of the funnel. When the ducks saw
it, their panic inside almost lifted the trap off the ground,

but the owl relentlessly forced its way through the funnel. As it emerged, every duck fell to the mud floor and lay silently awaiting what was now inevitable.

The next morning the men came to clear the trap. As the bow of their canoe rounded the bend, they sat stricken dumb. At first glance they appeared to have taken only one bird, but the floor of the trap seemed to have been strangely raised during the night. As they came nearer, they saw a great horned owl standing on a mat of dead ducks. Each had been cleanly decapitated.

The male black had seen the owl drop toward the trap not to rise again. Instinctively he drew close to the fringe of alders in case it came his way when it left. He remained for some time, afraid to cross the open water of the lake to join the others feeding in the shallows, but as time passed and the owl did not reappear, his courage returned, and he was with the others when the canoe pushed through the morning mists on its way to the trap.

They all rose together with a wild flapping of strong wings and circled over the lake. They watched the men enter the trap and kill the owl and begin the sad job of removing the headless bodies of their erstwhile companions. Suddenly a great longing to leave came over them. The leader swung and headed back to the sea, but instead of sideslipping happily down just beyond the breakers, she kept on with a strong steady beat, heading south.

Chapter Five

As they crossed the forty miles of open sea, the cliffs of the north shore of Anticosti Island slid beneath them. Over the muskeg-strewn interior where the man-made introduction of deer had so multiplied and depleted its food supply as to become runty and completely alter the composition of the forest, they flew until the south shore came into view. Here they broke formation and sideslipped down to a large tide pool on the beach.

On his last circle before landing, the male black swung out beyond the breakers; he was about to circle back to the beach when a strange sight below gave him pause. A number of white forms were sliding through the water ten feet below the surface but still clearly visible from the air. A school of white whales was following the capelin, and, as they slid smoothly up to the surface to blow, they rose right under the circling black. The gleaming ivory-white backs of the adults were visible for miles as they broke the surface, but the gunmetal-colored young were more difficult to see. They swept along the beach, following their food, and the black joined his companions in the tide pool.

Some of the geese were already there, and the blacks and greenwings joined them in the pools and along the mud flats as the tide ran out. The male black was picking up snails when he looked up in surprise as three deer stepped daintily across the beach and began feeding on the seaweed. This is one of the unnatural feeding habits deer on depleted range will develop. As the black had never seen this before, he watched them for some time until a fox came along and saw him, forcing him to move out to open water.

The next day they were strung out along one of the outer reefs at low tide when the male black was startled by the sudden appearance of a large head in the water amidst the feeding ducks. It swam to the reef, and the ducks and geese parted to let it pass. A great gray seal, eight feet long and almost a thousand pounds in weight, awkwardly dragged itself ashore over the slippery rocks. This giant among the seals of the Gulf was a year-round resident of its waters. It had few enemies besides man, and here on the south shore of Anticosti Island there were over one hundred and thirty miles of uninhabited shore where man rarely appeared from one year's end to the next.

In addition to the white whales, and very occasionally the deadly killer whale, the rorquals, those great fin whales that strain their food from the sea, and pothead whales with their bulging foreheads were to be found in the surrounding seas. In late fall some migrants from farther south also ended their journey here, among them the great white shark that is a menace to any seal. Even during the winter it was well to be on the lookout for the Greenland, or sleeper shark of northern seas, but on land man was the only foe.

The great beast dragged itself onto the rocks with a pathetically awkward and inefficient caterpillar motion. Unlike the fur seals, walruses, and sea lions of the Pacific, this seal cannot turn its hind flippers under it to move on land. When it reached a level spot, it rolled over on its back and began snoring steadily. The ducks and geese closed in to resume their interrupted feeding.

The manless idyll of Anticosti Island came to an end for the blacks when a cold front came down from Ungava and locked the freshwater pools in ice. The tide pools were still open of course, but the waterfowl had a long way to go, and the time for another move had come.

A powdering of stars was still visible in the western sky as the birds rose from the beach and headed out to sea, cleaving the sea smoke as they settled into a lop-sided V. Passing over the white whales, whose gleaming backs heliographed their farewell for another season, their strong wings settled into the mile-consuming beat of migrating black ducks. As the early-morning fog burned out with the rising sun, the high cliffs of Gaspé, with a sprinkling of fishing boats at their base, came into sight ahead.

As they swung in to the land they were greeted by the "Ow-owly, ow-owly, ow-owly" of a band of old squaws moving along the coast. A small group of the beautiful harlequin ducks, that are to the northern coast what the gaudy wood ducks are to the inland ponds and streams farther south, joined them at the outer reefs. They swept on down the shore, and as they passed a dory the boom of a ten-gauge shotgun leaped out. The harlequins were flying just abreast of the male black, and at the sound of the shot they all plunged from the air into the water at full speed. The gunner, elated at the wonderful success of his shot, grasped his oars and made for the spot. When he got there, there was not a duck in sight. Forty yards away the entire flock of harlequins leaped through the surface as if shot from a gun, and resumed its interrupted flight as the gunner stared openmouthed. A hoarse "Oy-oy-oy" followed by a loud clear "Qua-qua-qua" drifted down to him as they set out in pursuit of the migrating blacks.

They passed the deserted seabird cliffs of Gaspé and Percé Rock and arrived at the mouth of the Bay of Chaleur. Here some turned in to the bay, and others crossed to Miscou Island, heading for the long lagoons filled with eel-grass north of Miramichi Bay. The male was with this latter group which moved south, passing places with such wonderful names as Shippigan Gully, Pokemouche Gully, and Tracadie Lagoon. At Tabusintac Lagoon, the next stopping place to the south, they landed to feed amid the geese happily plucking eelgrass from the shallows.

The next morning gunfire was heard at daylight, and the geese and blacks rose and flew out over the barrier beach to spend the morning riding the seas beyond the breakers. For many years shooting here had been prohibited in the afternoons to allow the geese time to feed unmolested. They knew well when it was safe to return.

One day as he swam along the edge of the outer beach at Tabusintac, the male black came upon a bird swimming ahead of him, dragging one wing in the water. It dived awkwardly and weakly. As the black came up, he saw it was a cormorant. He thought nothing of it until he came to a second and then a third and fourth badly wounded cormorant trying desperately to survive despite crippling injuries. On the beach at high-water mark were row upon row of dead cormorants.

These were the result of one of the most inhumane practices still tolerated in North America. Each year before the duck season opens on October 1st, certain "sportsmen" of New Brunswick and adjacent areas go to Tabusintac and other places along the east coast of New Brunswick for their annual "shag shoot." Cormorants (shags) are easily fooled by silhouette decoys of their own species. Some outfitters of the region arrange blinds and decoys for visiting gunners at a fixed rate per day. There are no shooting hours, no bag limits, no season, no plugged guns—in fact, no restrictions of any kind, and two men may well use a case of ammunition in a day. The cormorant, being neither a game bird protected by local laws nor a migratory bird protected by federal law, has no protection whatsoever, and the slaughter is ghastly. The killing is carried out in the cruelest possible manner. The shore for miles below the blinds is lined with dead and dying birds; and as there is no thought of shooting cripples because this would be a waste of ammunition, the wounded are allowed to escape to die more slowly. The live-pigeon shoots of our grandfathers' time were outlawed seventy-five years ago on humane grounds, but the annual slaughter of inoffensive and harmless cormorants for nothing but the chance to practice on live birds before the waterfowl season opens still goes on in eastern New Brunswick.

The shooter packs his guns, rubs his sore shoulder, pays his bill, and departs thinking, Now I'm ready for the ducks.

On the beaches he has left, the dead begin to drift ashore

on the rising tide as the sun dips into the blacklands, or bogs, to the west. By morning many more will have died of belly wounds, and the last to die will be those broken-winged cripples slowly starving that the male black met a month after the last of the "shag shooters" had gone home.

They are the last of the birds of North America to be killed simply "for fun," with no one even bothering to pick them up. The locals try to justify this slaughter by claiming that the birds are serious competitors for commercial fish, but studies of food habits have not confirmed this. The sole benefit is a few more days' booking for a handful of outfitters.

The male black and his group were resting with the geese one morning beyond the breakers when some young geese grew impatient. None of the old geese would move, but the youngsters flew round and round, calling to them to rise and lead the way. As they flew over the group of blacks, their calls were answered from inside the lagoon. Without hesitation they flew off in that direction. The male black and two others leaped from the water and fell in behind.

The young geese remembered enough of their elders' training to flare high as they crossed the barrier beach. As they came over the lagoon beyond, they saw a group of geese clustered about what appeared to be a floating mass of eelgrass. One of these was calling stridently to the on-coming youngsters followed by the three blacks. Innocently the young geese flew directly to the caller, banking in a tight circle to land with their large feet extended. The blacks were a little above and behind, following the geese blindly.

As the feet of the leading goose touched the water, the mass of eelgrass erupted, and a gunner sat up in his sinkbox to swing on the leading goose. His first shot killed it instantly, and his second brought down the next in line with a broken wing. As he killed it with his third and last shot, the blacks clawed frantically for altitude over his head.

They bolted for the open sea. As they arrived, the adult geese were beginning to bestir themselves in preparation for the daily move to the feeding grounds after noon when the shooting stopped. It was safe then, but only the survivors of this year's crop would have a chance to learn this.

After two more morning flights into the lagoon, when birds on either side of him had been killed, the male black never entered until he was surrounded by veteran geese who talked confidently all the way in. Then, and only then, did he relax and stuff himself with the delicious eelgrass. Thus did he learn about sinkboxes, callers, and shooting hours. This knowledge would remain with him for the rest of his life.

His next stop was Miramichi Bay, where the hordes of salmon headed upriver to spawn in one of the greatest salmon rivers of the world. Along the outer bars a few great gray seals, similar to those he had known at Anticosti, lay stretched on the sand, barking gruffly. Occasionally they followed the salmon into the gullies, only to be caught in the fishermen's nets, with which they wrought havoc. Their other crime was that they were one of the hosts of the parasitic codworm, and a bounty had been placed on their heads by the Department of Fisheries. In consequence of this persecution, they were extremely shy and difficult to approach, and the blacks saw them hauled out only on the most inaccessible bars, quite unlike their behavior on Anticosti, where they were not hunted.

One day the blacks were resting outside the lagoon, sleeping with their heads under their wings. They drifted

on the tide close to a sandbar where lay what appeared to be a gray seal. It slept only seconds at a time, continually lifting its head to look around, grunt, and wave its flippers. Soon the head of another appeared nearby. Completely ignoring the ducks, who woke and watched it pass, it swam toward the seal on the sandbar. The grunting and flipper waving increased, and slowly the swimmer was lured in until it ran aground. Then, very slowly, the great beast began to drag itself out on the sandbar.

The seal on the beach flipped and grunted enticingly and rolled over several times away from the water. Eagerly the newcomer struggled in pursuit until it too was well away from the water. Suddenly the enticer lay still, and something happened under its chin. The skin parted, and the muzzle of a shotgun poked out. It steadied on the oncoming seal less than ten yards away, and a spurt of flame burst from it. The roar of the gun was almost lost in the bellow of pain from the great seal as the heavy ball broke its neck. It twitched convulsively and lay still, with blood pouring from its mouth. The hunter shed the rest of his cumbersome disguise and ran to it, drawing his knife. Grasping the great muzzle, he hacked and sawed at the tough skin until the snout came away in his hands. That night he would get ten dollars for it and the lower jaw from the Fisheries Protection Officer.

The blacks had almost fallen asleep again as the shot rang out, but they leaped into the air and flew off to join a multitude of frightened geese. For days afterward they watched the feeding gulls wheeling over the sandbar, but they never dared come close enough to investigate what they were eating.

After leaving Miramichi Bay, they flew leisurely down the coast, stopping to feed in the rich estuaries of the many small rivers that drain into Northumberland Strait. Reaching Cape Tormentine, they crossed overland to Baie Verte and from there to the isthmus between New Brunswick and Nova Scotia, where they settled into the marshes of Tantramar.

Here were many other blacks, mixed with teal and wood ducks, ringnecks and widgeon, or baldpates, pintails and goldeneyes. Soon the male's group was joined by a flight of blacks straight from the Codroy River in Newfoundland. The male black and two of his brood that were hatched at Lake Melville fed side by side in the same pond, although none knew of his relationship to the others. The male had circled the Gulf of St. Lawrence to the west, and part of his brood had gone to the east. They came together again at Tantramar.

Chapter Six

The Acadian explorer looked over his Micmac Indian's shoulder at the clouds of black ducks and Canada geese rising from the great marshes that stretched before them to the Bay of Fundy.

"Quelle tintamarre!" he exclaimed. What an uproar!

Today the only sound to be heard there is the sighing of the wind through the tall hay. The great Tantramar marshes have for the most part disappeared. The Acadians who settled there began at once to build dikes to hold back the waters of the Bay. They dug ditches to drain the marshes for farming, and gradually the great home of the waterfowl was whittled away. Two hundred years later the

Government of Canada is still engaged in diking and draining these marshes, and a sportsmen's organization, Ducks Unlimited, is endeavoring to preserve what is left of the waterfowl habitat. The Tantramar and Missiquash marshes on the Nova Scotia–New Brunswick border were in their pristine state among the finest marshes in eastern Canada. They were a natural concentration point for the waterfowl from the shores of the Gulf of St. Lawrence and the huge extent of country to the north and east. Gradually they have shrunk under the pressure of man's use until today the original meaning of the name Tantramar has been forgotten. The greatly diminished flocks using the area now still fly out to the mud flats bared by the highest tides in the world, but today their cries could hardly be called a "tintamarre." The only sound now is the whistle of the ever lonely wind through the hay barns that dot the flats.

The waterfowl habitat at Tantramar is now restricted to the rear fringes of the once-great marshes. Here the big male joined a group that knew the area well. They took him to a lake with several square miles of bulrush standing in permanent water. He quickly learned the spots the gunners favored. As there was still plenty of room here, he made his headquarters well away from the danger areas.

Another lake nearby looked equally inviting, but he found when he visited it that no good duck foods grew there. A long defunct sawmill had used the lake for many years as a dumping ground for sawdust, which formed the island on which he stood. In its slow decay, this material had changed the whole biological complex of the waters; the sawmill had destroyed the lake just as surely as the dikes had destroyed the marsh. As the circling black ducks flew over the white-painted houses of their competitors, they saw this great concentration point grow smaller year by year.

The group the male found himself with was led by an old and experienced female. Several times she called him back just in time as he was about to drop out of the flock to investigate a group of motionless ducks in an inviting cove, lured by the loud calling that came from their direction. Once he disregarded her; he and another duck swung low over one of these strange flocks. A man rose from the grass, and the black's companion crumpled, falling end over end into the cove as the crash of gunfire echoed over the marsh. The black, clawing frantically for height, felt searing pain cross his breast as a second shot sounded behind him. He felt the hot blood soaking his feathers, but terror lent him strength and he rejoined the flock. It was only a flesh wound, but the feel of the blood, as well as the pain, taught him caution as nothing else could.

Another day, as he was nervously catnapping on the end of a log, he was brought fully alert by the snapping of a branch in the bush behind him. He leaped into the air just as a gun crashed. The shot killed the next duck astern; but it had been aimed at him, and only his automatic re-action had saved him. The jump-shooter picked up his bag, not quite satisfied, as he knew the one he had missed was larger. The male never returned to the ponds, and flew far out to the seaward edge of a salt marsh, where he remained for the rest of his stay.

He spent some time at Tantramar before moving on to the next great bay to the west. Here too the tide ran out to expose red mud flats. The black found conditions much like those he had left at Tantramar, but with one major difference. One day at low tide he was dabbling for snails around a pool on the mud flats well up into the mouth of a fair-sized river that entered the Bay. As he was far from any dry land, he felt safe and relaxed. He was paying no attention to his surroundings, and the soft sound of rushing water meant nothing to him. Tipping up happily in a good colony of snails, his head was down when the tidal bore struck him.

Amazed and angry, he was tumbled several yards in front of the rushing wall of water before he could regain control and bob over the crest. There he found himself in the middle of a large expanse of open water too deep for him to reach the bottom. A moment before he had been paddling in only a few inches of water, but now, as he turned in all directions searching for his pool, it was nowhere to be found. His surroundings had changed in an instant from a string of tide pools on the mud flats to an expanse of deep open water. In time he gave up and flew to the shore to find a new pool that would not disappear.

He stayed in this land of tremendous tides and red mud until the cold north winds encrusted his feeding areas with ice. Then he moved again, flying in company with about fifty others along the Bay of Fundy coast of Nova Scotia until they reached the southern tip of the great peninsula. Here they entered an area of innumerable deep bays and inlets facing the open sea. His companions were all adults in full winter plumage now, the young birds having moved on to more southerly climates some time earlier. The local hunters passed the word that the "northern redlegs" were in. Men looked to their guns and their tolling dogs.

To understand what happened next we must go back to the days before the white men came. The blacks were now in the land of the Micmac Indians, where long ago skin canoes would put out from shore to leave hunters hidden among the ledges. These men were skilled callers; they imitated the cries of the ducks and geese to perfection. Birds answering the calls were met by a shower of many-pointed bird darts. Their skin and feathers were put to good use by the squaws after the rest had gone into the pot.

The Indians learned that both ducks and geese could not resist swimming closer and closer to a fox playing on the beach or hunting amid the seaweed at low tide. The birds would crowd in to the very limit of safety to see their ancient enemy. One day an Indian accompanied by his dog was walking along the beach. He sat down beside a boulder as the dog ran on, searching for crabs among the washed-up seaweed. A raft of ducks and geese immediately lifted their heads and began to swim in toward the dog. Soon they were lining the water's edge as he played in front of them.

The next day the Indian, well supplied with bird darts, hid among a group of boulders as the tide ran out. He held his dog on a thong until a raft of waterfowl swam by, then threw a stick into the water and loosed the dog. As it dashed forward, every head in the raft went up and the leaders turned toward shore. They swam steadily and un-afraid until they reached the water's edge, fascinated by the antics of the dog the hidden Indian kept playing in front of him; when they reached the waterline they were within easy range. In one swift movement the Micmac stood up and impaled three geese on his darts as they rose in a roar of wings and frantic alarm calls. Thus was born the "toll-ing" of ducks and geese as it is carried on in this region today.

The male was picking snails off the seaweed along a shoal with the rest of the flock all about him. He was full and feeling lazy, and his exploring bill was probing more in interest than in hunger. Nearby, one of the flock gave a note of mild alarm and sat with head held high, looking toward the beach as a brown farm collie ran out from some bushes and went sniffing along the shore. The collie found a stick, tossed it into the air, and rolled on it. Now every head in the flock was up as they all turned to watch, fascinated.

The dog rolled and pranced and tossed his stick. Imperceptibly at first, the flock started to move toward him. Without looking in their direction, the dog kept steadily at his game, while two hunters hidden in the bushes behind slid the safeties off their guns.

Because the innate caution of the male made him hold back, he was one of the last to start toward shore. A female led the swimming ducks, all bunched behind her, toward the dog. With every duck's eyes on the collie, the slight movement in the bushes beyond as the hunters raised their guns went unnoticed.

Though the leaders, who had almost reached the waterline, were now touching bottom, the dog still played on, taking not the slightest notice of them. The other ducks crowded in, straining their necks to see. The male at the rear had just decided to force his way to the front when a small crab, disturbed by the press of ducks' feet, darted past in front of him in a dash to escape. Although he was not hungry, he could not resist this tasty morsel; plunging his head underwater, he grasped it as it passed. At that instant two guns blazed from the bush, and two trails of death blasted through the close-packed flock. When the male jerked his head up, dropping the crab that had saved his life, dead and dying ducks were all about him. He leaped into the air with the survivors and fled headlong, but two more went down just before they drew out of

70

range. The brown collie, its tail waving, joined the hunters in killing the cripples and picking up the dead.

The remainder of the flock moved to some ledges well out in the bay to join many others of their kind assembled there. The geese poured in from the north; both ducks and geese found this well-stocked region much to their liking as their feeding areas did not freeze. There was no reason to go farther south, and they settled in for the winter, learning to avoid the local hunters with and without their tolling dogs. The season closed without undue losses. The male thrived mightily, and there were many females for him to choose from when the next pairing season began.

When the shooting was ended for the year and the guns were put away, the biologist who had banded ducks for the first time at Tinker Harbour in Labrador eagerly awaited any word of the birds he had banded in the north. As reports of birds shot wearing his bands came in, he plotted them on a wall map; the blacks showed that some went south by way of Newfoundland and the Codroy River and others turned west along the north shore to Anticosti and south along the west shore of the Gulf. At the Tantramar marshes at the head of the Bay of Fundy, both flights came together again and proceeded south along the shores of the Bay of Fundy and the New England coast.

Then one day he opened an envelope containing reports of two of his banded ducks that drew a whistle of surprise from him. He walked over to his wall map and stared at it thoughtfully. The returns were from two of the young pintails he had banded while still flightless with their mother in the creek behind the mud flats at Tinker Harbour. A month after he had banded them one was shot at the mouth of the Mississippi, and a few days later the other was shot on the Dart River in Devon, England. He whistled thoughtfully as he pondered the diverse directions those two young ducks must have taken on their first journey from Labrador. Obviously pintails used different migration routes than black ducks, but what drove that young bird on its first southward migration to cross the Atlantic? Was there a flight of pintails from Labrador to Europe?

Part 2

Chapter Seven

For the next three years the male black thrived mightily. He developed with tremendous vigor, and soon became larger and a pound heavier than other males of his own age. He mated with a new female each year, and she took him to places he had never seen. One season he molted in the ponds below the Blue Hills of Coteau in southern Newfoundland where the caribou summer. The next season he was on a lake amid the lush green countryside of Prince Edward Island. Each fall he wended his way south to the wintering grounds through the gauntlet of gunfire. Each time he was unscathed. Because he had seen his companions crumple and fall on either side of him on several occasions, he developed a sixth sense of caution that saved him time after time.

This winter he had been accepted by a mature female who would lead him on the journey of his life. They had moved north up the coast with the others bound for the northeast, but when they reached the lower Maine shore she would not follow the host further. Here she lingered and waited until a number of pairs had assembled. Then one morning, leaping into the air with her consort directly behind her, she circled over the flock, calling. Pair after pair rose and joined them, and soon the whole group was in the air.

With the others following, she turned and headed inland away from the coast. As the islands and the shore disappeared, the snow-covered farmlands gave way to the somber spruces of the northern forest, broken by the white patches of still-frozen lakes. Mile after mile of the great forest of northern Maine slid beneath their wings as they wended their way between the higher hills, following the valleys to the north. With the snow-clad summits of the Green Mountains of Vermont to their left and the bulk of Mount Katahdin rising like a block of ice cream into the blue sky to their right, they crossed one of the greatest roadless areas in the United States. They came out over the land of long narrow farms that is southern Quebec. They had been flying now for over seven hours, and it was a welcome sight when the great valley appeared in front, crossing their path from west to east, and the female leading the long V began to lose altitude. She glided over the broad river, still full of drifting ice cakes, and sideslipped gratefully down on a mud flat.

They had reached the St. Lawrence.

The mighty river flowed by in sullen gray, bearing the silt from the Canadian shield, the lowlands of the Great Lakes, and the forests to the edge of the plains. Where the ducks had landed, it flowed under a towering bridge between cliffs on either bank and around the foot of a great cape. Cape Diamond, named for the diamond-like crystals still to be found there, now holds upon its mighty shoulders the City of Quebec. The ducks waited for dark before flying over its busy waterfront and the crisscrossing ferries to the western end of the large island in the river below. Here they landed on the mud flats of the Island of Orléans, and the big male climbed upon a boulder to look around him.

Another black had climbed on the same boulder to look around more than two hundred years earlier. Anchored in the river between his position and the heights of Cape Diamond was a forest of masts of the British fleet carrying General Wolfe to the siege of Quebec. The sound of the cannonading brought all heads up in the flocks of blacks on the same mud flat on the Island of Orléans.

The wars of Europe had reached the land of the black ducks, and they rose in a cloud from the beaches of Boischâtel as the English redcoats waded ashore, fouling their smart uniforms in the sticky gray mud.

The pair and their following stopped and rested for some days in the channel between the Island of Orléans and the north shore of the river. Opposite the eastern tip of the island, the first of the Laurentian hills reach the St. Lawrence where the looming bulk of Cape Tourmente falls to the gray waters. Here, on the extreme end of the broad tidal marshes that stretch from Quebec to Cape Tourmente, is the resting ground of the entire continental population of greater snow geese. These beautiful white geese with their black wingtips land each spring for a final rest and feed here before taking off for the North. They fly over the high hills and endless forests stretching to the arctic tundra and beyond to the islands of the eastern arctic where they breed. Here for centuries has been their traditional resting area on both spring and fall migration.

These high arctic nesters have a very short breeding season and are thus very vulnerable to storms. A late blizzard may well destroy the year's crop of young, and a series of such seasons could have disastrous consequences for the species. For a long time they declined, and it was thought that the greater snow geese would follow the Labrador duck to extinction. They came in contact with gunners only on their winter range in the mid-Atlantic states and at Cape Tourmente. Strict controls were placed upon hunting; the man-made harvest could be controlled, but no one could predict the arctic storms.

However, it seems that the harvest was more important than the storms, for after it was controlled the geese began to recover. Today their numbers are the highest in living memory. It was to this vital feeding and resting grounds at Cape Tourmente that the female was leading the flock of blacks.

Unlike the snow geese, the blacks would not take off from Cape Tourmente and fly nonstop into the arctic. Rather would they dally along the St. Lawrence, letting the breakup get ahead of them so that there would be patches of open water along their route north of the great river. They traveled slowly downstream from feeding area to feeding area along the north shore.

One day after they had moved well to the northeast of Cape Tourmente, the big male and his mate were circling

over the river examining a beach before landing. Suddenly
all the blacks and Canada geese on it took off with a babble
of calls and beating wings. A man in hip rubber boots,
carrying a sack, came sliding across the mud to the edge of
the tide. Ahead of him two black ducks and a goose, unable to fly, were flapping and straining on the mud.

He quickly wrung their necks, removed a steel trap from
their legs, and dumped them in the sack; then he carefully
reset the traps and placed them on the mud.

He checked his trap line along the beach and returned
to the shore as the geese and ducks circled over the river.

As he reached solid ground again and scraped the heavy mud from his boots the waterfowl began returning to the edge of the tide in ones and twos, and finally in a cloud when the forerunners had settled safely.

In the Maritimes illegal spring shooting is still a hazard to the geese and ducks in some remote areas, but the use of steel traps is an innovation of the people of the lower St. Lawrence. This had become a standard spring hunt to them, and it was carried out annually. The arrival of the waterfowl provided the first fresh meat of spring in isolated villages, just as it had to the people of Lake Melville.

For three hundred miles the blacks wended their way northeast, with the south shore of the great river gradually dropping below the horizon. They wandered amid the rocky islands and shoals of the lower river, but they always returned to the north shore. On these islands the local black ducks often nested in loose colonies with the gulls and eiders, in striking contrast to the solitary well-spread nests of the mainland birds. Here the great black-backed gulls would patrol the shore, alert for any duckling alone, eider, black, or other seabird. Any found would be swallowed whole. But it was as if a bond held the female to the north shore. Several times she started up one of the great rivers flowing in from the North, but each time she turned back, as there was no open water inland.

In this way they reached Seven Islands Bay, the beginning of the Gulf. Here they paused for a few days. On the fourth day what she was waiting for arrived: a warm front came up from the south. With a cry almost of relief the female rose to follow it over the escarpment and on to the greatest lap of her long journey. Her mate, riding her slipstream, had two other pairs behind him when they started, but by noon of the first day one pair had already dropped out.

Northward, ever northward, she bored into the icy air. The forests thinned into the taiga, where scattered clumps of spruce stood in the valleys and the bare bones of the land showed through the snow on the hilltops. This land, perhaps the most desolate in all North America with the exception of the southwestern deserts, once held large herds of caribou.

These herds lived on the white moss that carpeted the land as far as the eye could see. In summer this thick carpet became as dry as tinder. Fires set by lightning, as well as those set by the Indians, either by carelessness or deliberately as signals, made great inroads into it. When the first scientific explorer entered this region he reported almost half the country burned over and the caribou disappearing fast.

This had little effect upon the northern Eskimo, for they were coastal people dependent upon fish and sea mammals, but to the Nascapi, the hunters of the barrens and the taiga, this spelled almost complete catastrophe. Whole bands starved to death, and in some cases cannibalism was all that allowed the survivors to reach breakup.

These fires, in perhaps the slowest growing region of North America, were enough to doom the caribou herds for many years to come. The famous crossing points where the Indian bands gathered for generations to spear a winter's meat were abandoned because the deer no longer came. Only the stone tent rings marked their sites.

The vast land was just struggling up from beneath its winter snows as the blacks crossed the height of land and dropped into the valley of the Kaniapiskau River. Here at last the rushing rapids and thundering falls were going the same way they were. Their mounting roar as breakup came welcomed the female to the land of her birth.

They followed the great river north to its junction with the Larch. From there for the last eighty miles they followed the combined stream with its Eskimo name of Koksoak (pronounced Coke-swack). They passed Crystal I, the abandoned ferry airfield of Second World War fame, on the left bank, and, farther on, the buildings and boardwalks of Fort Chimo on the right bank. Then, gratefully, the tired wings stopped their endless beating and set stiffly for the circling glide that ended at tidewater on Ungava Bay, six hundred miles north of their lift-off from Seven Islands.

The female was home, and her soft "Quack-quack" was answered by several pairs scattered over the tideflats. The big male gratefully rooted out some snails and amphipods from the seaweed, and began at once to replace the weight he had lost on the long flight.

Chapter Eight

All around, sounds of spring were in evidence. The barren rocks of the shores pushed up above the forty-foot tides. The water ran out with rushing tide rips leaving endless miles of bare mud flats greater even than those at the head of the Bay of Fundy. This was the promised land for shore-birds, and great wheeling regiments of white-rumped and semipalmated sandpipers swirled above the tide pools. A northern phalarope danced in circles, uttering its sharp "Kit!" A ruddy turnstone stalked along the margin chuckling "Keta Ket" to itself, and a semipalmated plover's plaintive "Chi-we" came from behind the seaweed-draped rocks.

The loud "Kee-ow, kee-ow!" of the herring gulls over-head was answered disdainfully by the low harsh "Kyow" of the great black-backed gull stalking amid the tide pools in search of stranded minnows.

For several days they rested and fed on the tideflats, regaining the energy burned up in their long flight from the St. Lawrence. Then the female became restless again. This time, however, she did not want to go far. She moved eastward along the shore a few miles until she came to the mouth of a small river draining into the bay. About a mile inland the last patches of stunted spruces appeared, for the timberline just reaches tidewater at False River. Here she and her big mate settled into a marshy meadow as a pair of rough-legged hawks screamed at each other high in the blue sky above. Sparrow-sized American pipits danced amid the caribou moss all about.

A black-backed robin thrust out his ocher breast, and proclaimed his territory loud and clear from the edge of the spruce clump. The dreamy lisp of a Labrador savannah sparrow was answered by the high clear "Teer" of a snow bunting. A soft "Whee-ah" from the spruces announced a gray jay, and the cowbelling of a raven sounded from up-stream. Horned larks sat on the glacier-scored boulders, and the whistling "Kee-kee" of the beautiful arctic terns sounded overhead as they searched along the stream.

A male snipe winnowed overhead almost continuously as it flew in great looping swings over the black ducks' meadow. The fast "Whee-oodle, whee-oodle, whee-oodle" of a greater yellowlegs sounded from the mud flats beyond. A pair of duck hawks nested on the cliff of one of the islands at the mouth of False River, and their oft-repeated "We-chew" was part of the orchestration of the birds.

The season of life had returned to the barren wastes

of Ungava, and in each tundra pool mosquito wrigglers by the billion hatched out. Mosquito soup would be the first food of the young birds, but for the rest of the season the relentless attacks of the insects would make all travel on land an unremitting horror.

The female at once began to hunt for a nesting site. She selected one on the edge of a spruce clump in the lee of a glacier-scored boulder that gave her protection from the ceaseless winds. She settled comfortably into the foot-deep white caribou moss and began to pluck her down. The male had circled about in her general vicinity. He noted with suspicion a strange bird that seemed to take an undue interest in his mate's actions. It was a dark seabird, a little larger than himself, with long falcon-like wings. It showed a flash of white on the wings, and its two central tail feathers were elongated and pointed. He was looking at his first parasitic jaeger, and one of its principal foods at this time of year was the eggs and young of other birds. Once when it approached the sitting female too closely he rose and drove it off. It screamed at him and easily evaded his rushes, and soared away, searching over the tundra to the north.

Some days later it came back when the female was sitting on a full clutch of eggs and when the male was away feeding along the beach. It circled once, and then, with a shrill scream, dived on the female. She met it with flapping wings and loud calls for her mate, but a slashing peck from the hooked bill drew blood from her neck, and the pirate bored in and shouldered her aside. Completely ignoring her frantic calls and feigning of injury, it broke each egg in turn and gulped down the contents. When the male returned, he found his mate walking around the ruins of her nest, making low noises in her throat.

A week later, her maternal urge still strong, she had started a new nest. This time it was in the heart of a spruce clump, and well protected from view from above. Her incubation was undisturbed except by the numerous lemmings that were running everywhere in their tunnels through the moss, as this was one of their periodic years of great abundance. Though they actually crawled over her back as she sat on the nest, her eggs were too big for them to molest amid an abundant food supply.

When the eggs hatched, she led the ducklings to a tundra pond where a wood frog sang his courtship song, although permanent ice was only two feet below. Here the male left them to molt, and he saw them no more. They were at the northern extremity of the black duck's range, and many hundreds of miles from any country he had ever seen be fore. As soon as his new flight feathers grew, he set off to explore.

His first journeys took him northwestward along the edge of the bay. He soon found himself traveling with other blacks who had just completed their molt and with some young of the year trying out their wings for the first time. Scoters and eiders, old squaws and harlequins were all along the shore, and movements in all directions were going on constantly. The short arctic summer was already drawing to a close in the islands across Hudson Strait to the north. The shorebirds were beginning to mass for their great trek that would take some of them half around the world to Patagonia. The mud flats were lined mile after mile with their regiments as they formed and milled and wheeled about, and overall the soft "Quack-quack" of con- tented black ducks feeding along the tide sounded from the shore.

One day he was loafing in a tundra pond behind the

beach when he heard a familiar sound approaching. It was the soft gabble of geese. He scanned the sky as the sound grew closer, for it told him this was a large group. But not a wing could he see. Suddenly there burst over the rise beyond the pond a sight he had never seen before. A large flock of flightless Canada geese and their nonflying young were running toward him. On they came in massed ranks while he stared fascinated. When they reached the pond they split and went on either side of it, reforming beyond and carrying on at a steady run over the next rise. When the flock finally passed, he saw the reason for its most unusual behavior. They were being driven, and the men who hoped to herd them into traps where they could be banded followed close behind.

However, these men had never driven Canada geese before. They had run blue geese and snows, but never the big black-and-gray honkers. After a mile or so of running, the young blues and snows would be so blown that they had to be picked up and carried to the banding site. Not so the Canadas. After a three-mile run that outdistanced the men, they reached the trap. The wise old leaders remained well outside the lead-in fences and, circling around them, continued on at a dead run across the bare rock ridges beyond until they disappeared in the distance.

The luckless banders sat down to recover their breath. The leader wrote in his report that it was just not practical to drive Canadas like other geese, as in this type of country they could outrun a man, and were apparently tireless.

The big male and his group were restless and never stayed long in one place. After a week they found themselves at the northwestern tip of Ungava Bay. To the west lay the cliffs of the south shore of Hudson Strait, and forty miles to the east lay Aktapok Island with its eight-hundred-foot cliffs and its murre colonies. He was standing one day on a shoal, picking indolently at a mass of seaweed with a group of oldsquaws all about him. When they swam on, he joined them and browsed among the weed exposed by the falling tide as they dived in deeper water beyond. The urge to wander was strong in him, and when they rose as a flock he jumped into the air and followed.

They circled over the outer reefs and then headed out to sea, flying due east. Within the hour the towering cliffs of Aktapok Island came into sight and were almost obscured in places by the clouds of murres flying about their colonies. Several miles from the island they passed a herd of walrus swimming steadily in the opposite direction. Each year this herd gathered at the Button Islands off Cape Chidley to the east and moved directly to Aktapok Island over a hundred miles of open sea. After a rest and a period of feeding along the east and north coasts, they moved on in their westward migration into Hudson Strait. It happened that the big male black and his companions were coming to Aktapok the day the walrus left.

Though the ducks swirled around the foot of the cliffs, they found no shallows there, and, moving on to the east coast, they came upon the hauling ground of the walruses. There were shallows here where the great sea mammals raked shellfish from the bottom with their tusks. The oldsquaws landed and began diving at once, but the black swam to the edge of the rocks and was soon filling himself amid the seaweed.

He had not gone far when a snort and a movement on shore caught his attention. A lone bull walrus was lying on the rocks ahead. He was an outcast who had wandered down from northern Baffin Island and joined the herd at the Button Islands. When they moved west to Aktapok he had followed, but he had slept through their departure that day and had been left behind. His sharp yellow tusks were badly scarred, and spread out at the points more than usual, but he had another characteristic that made him different from other walruses. He had lived through a series of heavy ice years in his northern range, and often the ice had prevented him from reaching his normal feeding grounds where he could fill up on shellfish. During these periods of hunger he had turned to the only other source of food—the sea mammals that lived with him in the arctic seas. Now he was an outcast among them. He had learned to kill and eat seals, and their blubber had stained his snow-white tusks yellow. Once he came up under a narwhal and disemboweled it with a slash of his mighty tusks. He dragged and rolled the carcass into shallow water where he ate the blubber and intestines, staying beside it until it was only shreds of skin and bones. The Eskimos knew his kind well, and shunned them as both dangerous to approach and not fit to eat.

Now the seal-eater had recovered from his swim from the Button Islands and he was very hungry. His taste for the shellfish that were his natural food had long since gone, and he looked for something bigger, with red meat and blubber. His gaze swept the bay in front of him and passed disinterestedly over the ducks and other seabirds feeding there. Unlike the killer whale, who can catch seabirds on the water, they were beyond his powers, and he passed them by.

The male black closely watched this huge beast that he had never seen before. He could not be sure whether it was dangerous to him or not, but he remembered the gray seals of the Gulf of St. Lawrence, and decided it probably was not. However, he gave it a wide berth.

Suddenly a puffing blow, followed almost immediately by a smaller, softer one, sounded behind him in the bay. Instantly the walrus was all attention. He shuffled to the edge of the rocks and stared out over the waves. Then the sound came again, and the ivory back of a white whale rolled in the gray water with a small gunmetal-colored calf at her side. They had turned into the bay and were fishing over the flats, oblivious to all around them. The walrus lowered its great bulk gently into the water and submerged with hardly a ripple in a show of stealth amazing in such a huge, clumsy beast.

The black sat with head erect, watching the approaching whales. The young one stayed close to the mother's side, blowing when she did, and heading straight toward him. Suddenly the water boiled beside the mother, and the grotesque head of the walrus rose beside her white back with both tusks sunk to the gums in the belly of the calf. Blood stained her ivory sides as the mother turned in a flash to protect her calf, but there was nothing she could do. Her small teeth were useless against the tough hide and masses of blubber of the walrus. He ignored her and turned toward shore with the already dead calf impaled on his tusks and clasped between his flippers. The frantic mother followed until she almost ran aground. She cruised up and down, searching as the great beast on the rocks tore her calf to pieces and ate gluttonously of the warm, bloody meat while the noisy gulls gathered for the feast.

A week later the black was back at the mouth of the Koksoak River. Finding little to his liking at Aktapok Island, he joined the first flock of sea ducks he saw returning to the mainland. The walrus would stay with its prey until little remained but bones, and then would set off on its lonely journey to the west to rejoin the rest of its kind. His was the life of the straggler, and it bothered him not at all to be left behind; but ducks love company, and the black was not long in seeking it.

The shorebirds had increased noticeably in the time he had been wandering to the north, and fall had now begun. He had moved about thirty miles inland to some lakes to the east of Fort Chimo, and he and some other blacks were feeding on the berries that dotted the tundra along the shore. Suddenly one of them lifted its head and gave a warning note. Some Eskimo women and children were slowly approaching as they too picked the berries. The blacks rose immediately and flew back to the center of the lake, and as the big male took wing a female pintail and a late brood of still-flightless ducklings ran to a nearby pond and plunged in.

The pond, however, was only about ten yards across, and the terrified duck with her brood close around her sat in the exact center as the Eskimos came up. Their discovery was greeted with a shout that brought them all running, and soon they surrounded the pond. The first hail of stones broke the wing of the female and killed two of the ducklings, and with gales of laughter the women and children stoned the last one to death. The female they brought home was worth eating, but the broken, bloody bits of fluff that had been the ducklings they left floating in the pond. No thought of the waste they had caused crossed their minds, and they gleefully exhibited their prize to their men. The meaning of the word "conservation" has not yet reached these people, although of all the inhabitants of North America the natives of Ungava, both Eskimo and Indian, would benefit by it most.

The group of blacks the big male found himself with had arrived at Ungava Bay overland from the east shore of Hudson Bay, and they would return the same way. The big male, being new to this far northern region, had no traditional routes to follow once he had left his mate, and he joined the group with no thought of where they were bound.

When the first frosts nipped the berries on the barrens behind Fort Chimo, the ducks turned up the Koksoak, away from the sea, and began their long journey south. However, there was none of the urgency about it that had marked the northward migration in spring. They would stay for several days in any area of good food they found before moving on to the next. Life was unburdened by the jealousies of courtship and territorial defense. Their only preoccupation now was food.

Chapter Nine

Up the Koksoak they flew until they reached the mouth of the Larch River coming in from the west. Here the leader turned westward and almost immediately flew over the first of the rapids. For the next forty miles the river was very rough as it tumbled down from the high country of the interior of the Ungava Peninsula. The blacks crossed this inhospitable country in one flight and settled that night in one of the big lakes to one side of the main river. They were following the tree line now, and to their right the barren interior of the huge peninsula stretched away to the horizon in gray plains of some of the oldest granite in the world, dotted with lakes in every fold of the land.

They dallied on the lakes at the head of the divide, some of which drained into Ungava Bay, while others ran west to Hudson Bay. The leader chose a westward-flowing river to follow when they resumed their journey. They were now in a region of large freshwater lakes connected by fast rivers. One day the big male was resting in a sheltered bay in one of these lakes where there were shallow water and some aquatic plants. As these were a rare luxury here, he had spent the day tipping up happily along the edge of the bay. He had noticed several broad trails in the mud crossing the shallows, and two circular beds where animals of some size had been sleeping.

He had just straightened up from one of his tip-ups with a beak full of weed when he became all alert. A large head rounded the point and swam steadily into the bay. A full-grown harbor seal swam to one of the well-used channels in the mud, and it suddenly saw the duck. A second seal appeared, and both sat upright in the water, curiously watching this intruder who was making himself so at home in their favorite sleeping spot. Finally they agreed he was harmless, and the two exceedingly rare Ungava freshwater-seals slowly entered the little bay.

These almost unknown seals live only in Upper and Lower Seal Lakes on the Hudson Bay side of the Ungava Peninsula. They remain all year round in the lakes, apparently having been isolated there since the last Ice Age. They live entirely on live fish. In winter they must concentrate at rapids that do not freeze, as they cannot keep breathing holes open through three feet or more of freshwater ice as can the marine seals of the high arctic in sea ice. In summer they have learned to use short portages across the rocky points that split their lakes up into many long bays.

Only on a few days each year is the weather bright and sunny. On these days they go ashore to sleep and sun themselves. It was only in 1942 that they were officially discovered and described by a scientist, although they had been known and hunted by the native Indians from time immemorial.

Having decided that the duck was harmless, the two seals caterpillared their way along the muddy channels until they reached the beds and placidly went to sleep. The big black watched suspiciously until all was quiet; then he too went peacefully to sleep side by side with the last large mammals to be discovered in North America.

A distant splash echoed across the stillness of the lake, and instantly all three were awake. A seal lifted a whiskered nose, and sniffed—then they both got it. The smell of smoke was drifting across the lake. Again a large splash sounded—and both seals were wriggling toward deep water. They dived and disappeared as soon as they reached it, swimming hard toward the fascinating sounds and smells that had piqued their curiosity.

The black rose from the shore and swung out over the bay. On a point about a mile away a canoe was drawn up on the beach and a large fire was burning nearby. The strong wind was blowing the smoke across the water, and an Indian stood on a rock, throwing large stones into the lake. Experience had shown that the seals could not resist coming to see what was making this fascinating combination of sound and smell on their silent lakes, and a second Indian with a rifle in his hands leaned across a boulder nearby.

The rock-thrower glanced up casually as the black swung over his point, but his eyes went quickly back to the lake before him, sweeping and searching.

Suddenly his chin went out and he called softly, "Atchook!" as a whiskery muzzle broke the surface.

The big black was half a mile down the lake when the rifle shot bounced off the silent hills. He did not look back.

This was the first shot he had heard since the previous fall, and it reminded him that the time of guns had come again. The ducks flew over the divide to the next river to the south where there was no sign of man, and settled for their next stop in another chain of connecting lakes at the head of the Little Whale River.

Here again the curious landlocked seals bobbed up to watch as he and his companions slid in to feed in the shallows. A fox in full fall pelage watched from the shore with hungry eyes, but none of the ducks gave him a chance.

When they resumed their journey they followed the river out to the coast of Hudson Bay and turned south once again on salt water. They passed Duck Island and Boat Opening, Castle Island and Schooner Opening, Merry Island and Sandy Point, and they were well on their way to Cape Jones—the entrance to James Bay. They pressed on past Bear Island and Humbug Harbour and entered Long Sound, at whose western end lay the great Cape.

As they approached, the leader turned inland and led them across a stony flat that lay behind the outer headland. This was a traditional shortcut used for centuries by the ducks and geese to avoid the usually bad winds at the outer cape—and it had not gone unnoticed. The sharp-eyed Crees who hunt this coast had erected permanent stone blinds across the flat to pass-shoot the unsuspecting ducks and geese returning from the North each fall. It was toward this string of blinds the leader was now taking his flock. Because none of the veterans had heard gunfire for ten months—and the birds of the year had never heard it—their guard was down.

When the gray flat unfolded beneath them with the piles of rocks at intervals it looked no different from the hundreds of miles of barrens they had already crossed. Not a movement showed from the veteran Cree hunters concealed in each rock pile, and the ducks were flying low and slowly into the strong wind. As they came over the blinds, the hunters rose as one and poured in a volley.

The duck immediately ahead of the big male was dead before his wings folded, and half the flock was cut down at once. The big male escaped the first volley, but as he was frantically clawing his way into the sky, going almost straight up, a stunning blow hit his left side, and once again he felt the trickle of hot blood in his feathers. The great drive of his wings faltered for an instant, and then recovered, and he kept on going with all his might until he had reached the coast again beyond the deadly shortcut. Here the survivors landed well out to sea.

The cold salt water soon staunched the flow of blood from the wound in his breast, but when the ducks moved on he swam to the shore and crawled between two boulders and was seen no more by the flock. He rested for three days, and the wound rapidly sealed. When he tried out his wings the wounded breast muscles hurt badly at first, but after he was properly warmed up he could fly almost as well as ever, and once more started south.

At the mouth of the Comb River he joined a mixed flock of black ducks and blue geese who were milling about on a bar. Two of the survivors of his original flock were still there, and he joined them when the flock rose and headed out to sea. As he had never seen this part of the country before, he had no idea where he was going but was content just to be with others of his own kind.

Flying low over the water in a cold rain, they crossed the fifty miles of foggy sea to the Twin Islands—the southernmost outpost of the arctic. The two-hundred-foot ancient sea cliffs, now separated from the tidewater by a mile or more of wide terraces, show that these islands have risen or that the water level of James Bay has sunk. Whichever happened has produced ideal denning sites for arctic foxes and polar bears in the rims of the terraces. The most southerly pairs of polar bears in the world breed there where the cold north winds blow almost without stopping, and the black ducks, green-winged teal, and Canada geese come each season to breed and keep them company.

As the flock wheeled in to land, a great shaggy mass of dirty yellowish fur sprawled on the rim of the beach stirred. Two keen black eyes in the snakelike head of a polar bear swung around to watch them. Earlier in the season, when the ducks and geese were nesting, the bear made a regular habit of hunting out nests and eating the eggs. He had accounted for many, but now that they were all flying they no longer figured in his diet. He watched as they landed and swam to the shore; but he had long since learned the futility of trying to stalk them, and he rolled over and went to sleep. An arctic fox attempted a stalk, but it was soon detected and the ducks withdrew to an offshore bar to feed unmolested.

The driving icy rain from the North pelted down as the ducks left the Twins and started south over the islets and shoals of James Bay. They were safe amid these isolated shoals miles from shore, but even the ducks and geese were looking for better weather. They pressed on until they reached the great marshes of the mainland at Hannah Bay, a traditional resting area for the geese from the high arctic.

Over the endless miles of salt marsh the geese traded back and forth, calling, calling, as new groups came in daily from the north. The waveys, or blue geese, were there in great numbers, as well as the Canadas; and blacks, pintails, and teals fed happily in every creek and pond. There was only one flaw in this haven—the gunners were there too, and their Indian guides were expert callers.

The big male black heard a lone goose calling time after time. He saw passing flocks swing over to investigate, only to be met by gunfire and leave some of their number as crumpled blotches of white and gray on the flats. It was the very numbers of the geese that saved the ducks. Several times he had passed over a cluster of white objects on the ground he had mistaken for geese, as one was calling persistently, not knowing they were clumps of mud wrapped in paper. All that saved him was a gang of geese coming in low to the call, and the gunner held his fire.

After a stay of a week at Hannah Bay, he found himself with a group of blacks flying up the Harricanaw River toward the height of land. They beat steadily across the low country around the bay and over the endless forests of the Abitibi Territory. That evening the big male stood on the end of a point jutting out into a lake as the lonely calling of the loons echoed off the silent hills. A pair of the great divers had nested on a tiny islet in the middle of the lake that year, and their lone offspring had just learned the difficult art of the long running takeoff these birds need to become airborne.

They were preparing to leave this lake where their

presence had had a marked effect upon some of its other inhabitants. In a deep cleft in a split boulder on the bottom, only a few yards from the point where the big black stood, a broad tail waved slowly from side to side as a great trout maintained its position in its lair. Barely moving its fins and tail, it lay waiting for anything alive that was small enough to swallow to cross the mouth of its hiding place.

It was the largest trout in the lake, and although it was too big for the loons to swallow, it had noted the intrusion of these great spotted "fish" into its domain shortly after the ice went out in the spring. The ringing calls and loud laughter that rolled across the lake could be heard by the trout when it hunted near the surface during the spring nights. It had no way, however, of connecting these curious sounds with the strange streamlined creatures that plunged through the silver roof of its world and consumed quantities of the smaller fish that were its own food.

Later in the spring a female black duck had led her brood of downy ducklings to the lake. The big trout had regarded them with suspicion at first, but its interest quickened when it saw one of the ducklings dive to the bottom in two feet of water and seize a tadpole. Stealthily it moved closer and watched more carefully as again the duckling dived and brought up a leech. The third time it dived there was a flick of the muscular tail, the large mouth opened, and the duckling disappeared down the red throat in a rush of water as the great trout inhaled its prey.

The stock of small fish in these northern lakes is not large, and the effect of the loons' insatiable appetites soon began to be felt by the other fisheaters, among them the great trout. Its food was approximately the same size as that of the loons, and as this became scarcer the trout began following the duck brood as it cruised the shoreline. By the time the ducklings were too large for the trout to swallow, the brood was reduced to three.

The big trout was weakened by the loons' consumption of the food supply in his lake. That winter he was too sluggish to escape a wandering otter who caught him in a shallow bay under the ice. For many years thereafter the lake was safe for ducklings, and it would remain so until the meager food supply recovered and was able to support another large trout.

Unlike the trout, the loons were not confined to one lake. The following year the ice covered the loons' islet when they arrived, but to shift to the next lake was but a matter of minutes, and their breeding activities continued without a break. That year the female black duck nested on the ridge between the two lakes, and when the time came she led her brood to the closer of the two, which was the one the loons were using. The male loon thrust his daggerlike bill flat on the water when he first saw them, and rushed forward, scattering the brood. They quickly re-formed and scurried away from this great bird with the fierce eyes who drove them across the lake away from the vicinity of his nest. Henceforth they avoided that part of the lake.

On several occasions the snakelike black head had risen quietly to the surface and watched the downy ducklings as they paddled in the shallows. It noted that they dived freely after all sorts of aquatic life. One day a great swirl disturbed the water among the feeding ducklings, and the female caught a glimpse of a mottled side just as a powerful stroke of a webbed foot drove it under. The brood scattered, and when they returned to the duck there was one less duckling. The loon surfaced a hundred yards out in the lake, flexed its long neck, and snapped its sharp bill as he lifted his mournful cry to his mate across the lake.

The plankton of this lake was poorer than that of the first, and because of this there were no large trout to menace the ducklings. But there were also fewer trout to feed the loons; the great divers had turned to what was available and become duckling predators themselves. Thus did they cancel out their benefits to the ducks of one lake by destroying those of the next.

Beyond the height of land the blacks dipped down to the headwaters of the Ottawa and followed this great river back to the St. Lawrence. When the big male landed on Lake St. Louis, he had completed a circuit of two thousand seven hundred miles north of the river that season. He had almost recovered from his wound, but the pellet was still in his breast muscles, in the process of being encased in scar tissue where it would remain for the rest of his life.

When they left the St. Lawrence they followed the valley of the Richelieu River to its head in Lake Champlain —and unknowingly they were following a historic route.

A French explorer pushing south from the St. Lawrence with a war party of Indians glanced up at a long line of black ducks heading upriver ahead of him, and wondered whence they were bound. He looked around at his companions, each in a separate canoe of their native escort, each grasping his arquebus. They were on their way to their first meeting with the dreaded Iroquois, where they would give them their initial lesson in the effect of gunfire. When they debouched onto a great lake, black ducks were all around. As they were a war party in hostile territory, they traveled only at night, and tried to avoid frightening the ducks feeding along the shore.

The Iroquois were encamped at the end of a point jutting out from the western shore, and the prowling war party was discovered as it slunk silently along at ten o'clock at night. At once the silence was broken by the howls and whoops of both parties to raise their own courage and to terrify the enemy. By mutual consent the battle was adjourned until daylight, and all night long the dancing and howling went on.

At first light, hostilities began. The French leader marched up to within thirty paces of the three Iroquois chiefs positioned at the head of their men. The Iroquois stared at this strange creature from another world in his light armor, holding his arquebus—to them a totally unknown weapon; then their bowmen poured in a volley. The stranger took deliberate aim at the principal chief, and at the shot he and one of the lesser chiefs fell. The Frenchman had put four balls in his weapon, and he made a double first shot that removed the Iroquois leadership. His companions now opened fire from the woods, and the opposition bolted. Thus, by aiding them against their traditional enemies, the Iroquois, the French cemented their leadership of the Indians of the lower St. Lawrence.

The French leader said, "This place, where this charge was made, is in latitude forty-three degrees and some minutes, and I named the lake Lake Champlain"—after himself. The year was 1609, and black ducks were not to hear gunfire there again for a very long time.

Following south through the Hudson Valley, the blacks reached the coast. One day in late November the big male joined a flock that slid confidently in to land near a seawall with a city showing on the hill behind it. As cars were passing, this seemed to him to be a highly dangerous place, but when several days had passed and he had not heard a shot he realized he was safe, and relaxed.

Later, to his astonishment, he saw a group of black ducks and scaup swim toward a man leaning over the seawall. On the water below were a number of small red dots that the ducks were eating greedily. As soon as the man left, the black's curiosity got the better of him and he swam in to investigate. The red dots were cranberries the man had thrown to the ducks, and he gobbled them down with the others. Each day for a week the man appeared and fed the ducks and day by day their caution lessened.

One day, when the big male had been off on an excursion down the shore, he did not get back until after dark. He swam to the feeding place to see if any of the delicious cranberries had been left over. As soon as he came close he heard a sound that alerted every nerve in his body. It was the splashing and floundering of terrified ducks that were trapped. It was the same sound he had heard and helped to make when he had been caught in the banding traps.

The situation this time, however, was different. There was no wire enclosure here, and the ducks seemed completely free—yet they could not leave. They strained and fluttered, and each held his bill open in a peculiar way. Once he caught a flash of red in an open bill, as if the duck had a cranberry in its mouth—and so it had. The duck feeder had come later than usual that day and had flung a handful of cranberries to the waiting birds; then he carefully uncoiled lengths of fishing line and baited each hook with a cranberry. These he tossed out amid the others, and quietly retired. After midnight he returned; the cranberries were gone, but a black duck and a scaup were securely hooked, and he quickly pulled them in and wrung their necks. He barely glanced at the figure of a large black duck swimming at the outer limit of visibility. It rose cleanly into the night sky when he came over the seawall.

Thus did the big male return to the winter range after his longest journey in the North. He would carry a pellet in his breast for life as a memento, but since it had healed he was in no way incapacitated, and he faced the coming winter with undiminished vigor.

Chapter Ten

This year was to be a very special one for the waterfowl of the northeast coast. Cold came down from the North early and stayed for longer periods than anyone could remember. By the beginning of January the marshes were frozen solid, and would not break up again for two months. The ducks crowded to any fresh water still open, but soon the food supply began to dwindle. The accessible areas were exhausted first, and as the birds moved in desperation to the less accessible ones these too became depleted. By the end of January groups of starving ducks ringed every hole in the ice.

The game wardens watching their charges saw what was

happening, and raised the alarm. Soon articles appeared in the papers, and the conservation-minded public was aroused to the plight of the ducks. As quickly as possible an emergency feeding program was organized by the Game Department and conservation groups, and grain was bought and brought to the shore. Already ducks had begun to die, and each tide brought new bodies to the beach. Many more were too weak to move any distance to reach the food, and the problem was how to bring the two together.

By using boats and planes, every effort was made to get the grain within reach of the starving birds. Some of these efforts were successful. A few good meals of grain were enough to pull those who got it back from the sure death that awaited them, but despite all efforts there were many who never reached the grain—and never saw the breakup that spring.

The big male entered the period of starvation tough and strong and as well prepared for it as he would ever be. He had more vitality than those less well endowed, and as he grew weaker lesser birds died all around him. Crows came to pick at the carcasses of the dead, and a passing bald eagle, finding a winter's food supply, settled in for the season.

At last a boat appeared, skirting the edge of the ice, and a muffled figure in the bow raised his binoculars. He sighted the group of ducks, but as the boat came alongside, the big male drew on the last of his strength and rose into the air. He could fly only about twenty yards to the open water where he watched as the men scattered grain among the huddled figures on the ice too weak to attempt to get out of their way.

When they left, the big male swam back to the others on the ice. The yellow grain caught his attention at once—but something within him froze. This was the delicious stuff that had lured him into the trap, and for a long while he held back as his starving companions, with no such scruples, greedily gobbled it up. At last he could hold back no longer. Just as the candle of life within him was beginning to flicker, he stuffed himself with the life-giving grain. At intervals the boat came back and replenished their supply until the survivors were able to fly. Then they left the ice edge lined with their dead and passed on to the south, out of the region of permanent ice. Here they quickly picked up the normal pattern of their lives—in all but one thing.

As the days lengthened and the first inklings of spring appeared, the pairing season came into full swing. For the first time since reaching adulthood, the big male felt hardly any of the old urge to mate. The courting parties flew around the survivors of the starvation region to the north, but they all seemed dull and apathetic. Too much of their energy had been drained in the desperate fight for survival, and many would not breed that year.

The big male, with his better than average strength and resilience, took no part in the early courtship activities, but as the pairing season was drawing to a close he felt a slight resurgence of the old urge. Many pairs had already left for the North, but he felt no inclination to follow. He hung about the marshes until nearly all had gone, and then one day he met a lone female who did not appear to want to lead him anywhere.

After a few rather desultory head bobs and the bare minimum of a courtship flight with no competition, she accepted him as her mate. They moved back to the same marsh where he had found her and resumed their placid feeding. He was not yet fully recovered from his ordeal, and this arrangement suited him well enough.

This spring lacked the hectic qualities of far journeying that had been his lot in all the others, and everything went calmly and smoothly. During the month when the others were flying from one patch of open water to another across southern Canada, he and his mate fed and loafed amid the hundred-mile-long string of gullies and marshes that is the Barnegat Bay country of coastal New Jersey. Because there was a fair number of blacks that stayed here all year round, they did not lack for company.

The big male had all but recovered from his winter ordeal now, and he was appreciably larger than the local males. An old bayman saw him and remarked that he must be a northern redleg that had not gone north that season. The man noted that the big duck was paired, so he knew that this was no dying cripple but one who would be away again to the North the following spring.

As the time approached for her to nest, the female drew him toward a creek mouth beyond which she had nested for the past three seasons. He followed her dutifully as she led the way up the creek, but his reluctance mounted as he saw where she was taking him. Where last year there had been a secluded marsh in which she had successfully reared her brood and molted, today there was earth-moving equipment at work filling in the marsh. The flat surface of the new land behind was already subdivided into building lots.

She circled disconsolately at dawn and dusk for several days, searching vainly for landmarks that were gone forever. Finally she gave up and left the creek for good. Many other females were suffering the same fate as the irresistible approach of civilization destroyed their traditional homes and altered the land so that it would be forever useless to them. They wandered off to strange places and nested wherever they could, but, because of their unfamiliarity with the new areas, many were found by the local predators.

The female landed on the end of a sandbar jutting out into the bay. A few tussocks of sawgrass fringed its top, but otherwise there was no cover. She would normally shun such a location, but this year her entire world was in turmoil and the loss of her traditional nesting place had disrupted her whole set of values.

She walked across the beach toward the grass, leaving her mate at the water's edge. She had almost reached it when a bird fell screaming from the sky; she just managed to dodge the jab of a sharp beak. The tern rose with a loud scream and wheeled for another attack. It was joined at once by a second, and then a third and fourth. The duck beat a hasty retreat to the water, and they both swam off, glad to leave behind the hornets' nest of breeding terns they had disturbed.

They spent the night across the bay from the tern colony. Just before dawn the ringing screams broke out again, and the air was full of diving, yelling birds. A brown object writhed beneath the milling pack, biting and clawing at the plunging forms, but soon it was covered with blood and dragging its entrails. At the edge of the grass it died under the assault of furious jabs at its eyes and the base of its skull. The big Norway rat's body joined the debris of the colony.

The next night a mink wandered along the shore until it smelled the colony. It reached the first nest and killed the incubating bird before the defense was alerted, but

111

when the avenging squadrons arrived a mad dash and a plunge into the bay were all that saved it from the fate of the rat. It never again tried to catch nesting terns.

Through all this the big male felt strange and out of place. He had never before experienced a spring that drifted so rapidly into summer; the first really warm weather came well over a month before he was used to it. In this busy area he was rarely out of sight of man or his works; fishing boats and cars, as well as trains and planes, became more familiar to him than ever before. He lost some of his shyness, but he never relaxed his vigilance. While men often approached closer than he had ever before permitted, none got there without his knowing it and his watching their every move.

As the heat of summer advanced, he molted and began spending more and more of his time out on the open bays toward the ocean beach. Here the sea breezes made it cooler than the still, stifling marshes broiling under the midsummer sun. His flightless period had begun and he had joined a group of other males loafing away the days in which they were bound to the water in one of the big bays behind a break in the barrier beach that left a pass to the ocean. Through this pass the water rushed with every turn of the tide.

One breathless evening in midsummer he had been lying with his head under his wing, asleep for hours in the center of a raft of his fellows. He slept as soundly as he ever did, safe in the security of the others. The tide had changed an hour before sunset, and the flow was gathering strength as the shadows lengthened. Terns wheeled overhead, diving on the silvery minnows over the tideflats, and great dark stingrays plowed along the bottom. The shore fish came through the pass in schools to reap the harvest of the rising tide. As the water deepened over the flats, a strange object appeared riding the flow through the pass. It was triangular in shape, and it glistened darkly in the last of the light as it moved steadily ahead, cutting a clean V on the surface. It was the tip of the dorsal fin of a six-foot tiger shark.

When it cleared the pass, the shark turned along the outer edge of the bay where the water was now deep

113

enough to float it. Here it came upon a stingray lying submerged in the sand with only its eyes showing; but the shark was not deceived. The great blunt snout tilted down, and the ray made off with its wings beating frantically, but there was no escape. The shark overshot it on its first run, made its wide turning circle, and came in again. It seized the ray by one wing, completely ignoring the saw-edged poisoned dagger in the base of the tail that lashed ineffectively about. With a shake of its head it bit out a semicircular piece, like a cooky cutter, that ended any attempts to escape. With two more bites the ray was devoured completely, and the thrashing of the shark's heavy tail caused a splash and ripples that spread over the glassy surface of the bay.

As the moon rose and the tide reached its full height, the water on the inshore edge of the bay became deep enough to float the shark. The ducks were getting ready to feed now, and some of the young birds that could fly had joined the flightless adults. As they engaged in much chasing about, flapping along the surface, and rough play, the sound of their splashing carried far in the stillness—both above and below the surface. The shark was cruising leisurely just inside the outer beach when the sounds of splashing reached it. At first it simply slowed down and sank below the surface; then the fin reappeared, crossing the bay like the point of an upthrust knife cutting through a sheet of burnished silver.

The ducks on the edge of the raft saw it coming, but as the fin was smaller than they were it did not appear dangerous and they did no more than move out of its path. At that moment two young blacks started on one of their wild chases, flapping along the surface. At once the fin disappeared, and seconds later the great blunt snout of the shark reared from the water beside the hindermost duck, which disappeared still flapping as the terrible kukri-shaped teeth clashed together.

The big male black was but ten feet distant when the shark took the duck, and as he was still flightless he and the others unable to fly dashed madly for the marsh edge a hundred yards away. Some dived in their panic: their doom was marked by great swirls on the surface as the shark overhauled them and gulped them down one by one. The big male did not dive, but swam for his life with feet and wings. Twenty yards behind him the fin again broke the surface. It swung into his wake and slid forward, slipping through the water with hardly a ripple. As the gap closed rapidly, the black sensed he was being pursued. When he was ten yards from the marsh, but only ten feet in front of the shark, a great commotion exploded in the water behind him. Spray and mud flew high in the air from the madly lashing tail as the shark drove hard aground—at high tide. The black dived ten feet into the vegetation before he came to a halt. He lay there for a long time before his heartbeats returned to normal. Then he wormed his way gratefully farther into the marsh.

All that tide the shark thrashed and splashed, but he only dug himself deeper into the mud, where he died next morning when the ebb ran out, leaving him high and dry.

When the male black regained his powers of flight, he left the bay where he had caused the death of the shark. Unlike many of the young birds who move north in late summer as soon as they can fly, he turned south. He followed the coast to Cape May and across the wide mouth of Delaware Bay. He passed Cape Henlopen and followed on down the shore until he came to the bottom of the forty-mile-long Chincoteague Bay. Here he joined the first group of blacks he saw, and followed them as they crossed overland to that mecca of waterfowl from all over northern and eastern North America—Chesapeake Bay.

This great bay, the largest of the drowned valleys along the Atlantic seaboard, has a shoreline between four thousand and five thousand miles long. The distance from the capes to the head of the bay is one hundred and ninety-five miles. The total length of navigable waters in the bay and its tributaries is over one thousand seven hundred and fifty miles. Here ducks and geese have wintered in thousands since the last Ice Age, some coming from as far away as Alaska, and some being year-round residents that never leave.

The sport of waterfowling was developed to its highest degree here where the gunners had birds from more than half the continent to choose from. Soon the choicest localities were bought up by duck clubs, and many baymen earned their whole living as club employees. Elaborate blinds, sinkboxes, and sneak boats were designed; decoy making became a fine art. Stake blinds were permanently erected and maintained out on the flats. Some were mere boxes; others were covered with brush to make them look more natural. When the northerners departed each spring, the local females sought out these brushy blinds and built their nests in them. Thus did they serve both as hatcheries and as places of execution in the fall.

The big black and his group followed up the eastern shore and settled in one of the brackish estuarine bays where they filled up on claspingleaf pondweed, widgeon grass, and eelgrass. Such choice foods surrounded them in thousands of acres, and the huge outer bay and its tributaries provided many miles to wander over.

As summer ended and the first of the northern migrants, the blue-winged teal, arrived on the marshes the baymen were busy rebuilding blinds felled by winter storms and summer hurricanes since the previous fall. Fresh brush was added to the blinds where needed, and the decoys were checked over and repainted. Anchors and lines were inspected, and all the finer pieces of the duck hunters' equipment came in for their yearly overhaul.

The big male had been seen by several baymen, and his size in comparison with the local young birds commented on. Several went out of their way to note the creeks and gullies he was using, and some swore he was as large as a brant. He had no enemies now to bother him, and his life was a carefree round of feeding on the choicest of duck foods and sleeping undisturbed in any one of a hundred safe loafing spots. Thus passed the early fall.

Then one day the first shot echoed over the marshes. It was followed immediately by gunfire from all directions, and the season was opened. Ducks rose all around the black, and circled wildly—the young birds flying about investigating the groups of strangers that had appeared overnight in their midst. They were met with gunfire, and left some of their number behind at each set of decoys, but the adults, having been through this before, circled high and withdrew to the open water where they could not be approached. The big male was among the very first to settle on the bay.

On the second day of the season he rose from the marsh where he had been feeding at the first rosy flush in the eastern sky and circled out to the bay. He swung along the

117

marsh edge over the tideflats where stake blinds were dotted over the shallows. He carefully picked his way between them, being always careful to stay out of range of each in turn.

A dart of young ducks came wheeling in from the flank, gladly formed up behind this able veteran and followed wherever he went. He paid no attention to them, and together they wove their way between the blinds. As they came to the last the big male saw at once the set of decoys that surrounded it, and swung away, but the young bird next behind ignored him, set its wings, and swung in to the decoys. The rest of the flock followed despite the warning note uttered by the big male. They circled once and lowered their feet to land.

He swung high and watched as the first birds touched the water. As they slid forward on their bellies, two gun muzzles and the heads and shoulders of two gunners rose from the blind. The first two shots killed and leading pair on the water and the second two brought down a duck apiece. One hunter was shooting an automatic; his third shot went wide as the survivors climbed. He calmly reloaded and reshot a cripple, then he and his partner smiled and reached for the Thermos bottle.

The male, watching from afar, wondered why the young birds had disregarded his warning, which had been given in plenty of time, and had gone on to their deaths. He could not know that the two leaders had been hatched in that blind six months before and had spent all their lives until they could fly in its immediate vicinity. When they returned and found it surrounded by ducks, it was only coming home to them, and there was no question of following him further. They had gone home—and ended their short lives within a few yards of where they had begun.

When the big black had gone south past Cape May and into the Chesapeake country, he had left the main winter range of the blacks from the Northeast. Those wintering on this section of the coast were from the center of the continent and the James and Hudson Bay drainage. They were the western segment of the black-duck population.

As they poured into the bay country he once again met large males of his own size, travel-wise veterans who knew the danger spots between James Bay and tidewater on the Chesapeake. Gladly he joined their ranks, becoming indistinguishable among them.

One day his group alighted in one of the brackish estuarine bays not far from a group of large white birds that he had never seen before. He was reminded of the snow geese on the St. Lawrence, but these were larger and had much longer necks. They were eating widgeon grass and sago pondweed, two of his favorite foods, and he swam over curiously and attempted to join them.

The great white birds were whistling swans, some of whose relatives are said to be the oldest living animals, passing three hundred years in age. The nearest fixed an unfriendly eye upon the presumptuous black approaching. As it drew near, the long neck of the swan drew back into the coiled shape of a striking snake, and with a loud hiss it darted at the duck. The attack was so unexpected that the big male was caught off guard and received a painful peck that cost him some feathers before he could get out of reach. Never again would he approach these stately white giants so nonchalantly. Their disposition was irritable, and they had the power to enforce their wishes. After this, he left them strictly alone.

That year he survived the local hunters unscathed, and prepared to winter with more than a million ducks and geese, many of which he had never seen before. Blue geese were strange to him, and gadwalls, shovelers, and American widgeon he had seen only as rare stragglers. Here they were in large flocks, but the redheads, canvasbacks, ruddy ducks, and coots were all new to him. He thrived in this water-fowl paradise well south of the killing frosts that had so nearly ended his days the year before.

As fall lengthened and the peak of the shooting passed, loose pairing began among some of the blacks. He was fully recovered now and, when he showed interest in a female, his magnificent bulk discouraged any lesser male. He was accepted by the first female he courted, and she led off feeding along the shore. It seemed that his mating problems for another year would be easily solved, but he could not know their relationship was to be of short duration.

Chapter Eleven

One day they both awoke on their resting bar to find heavy rain falling. The wind built up in strength until it was blowing a gale, driving the deluge almost horizontally across the pond. At once the female became alert, and communicated her alarm to her mate. But as he was a veteran of many North Atlantic gales on his home coasts to the north, he found no cause for undue alarm here. They huddled on the sand in the lee of a driftwood log and prepared to let the storm blow itself out. He put his head under his wing and prepared to go to sleep.

But this was no ordinary gale. A tropical hurricane with winds of over one hundred miles an hour at its center was coming north up the coast. Before it fled birds of all sorts from the south, and great numbers of waterfowl moved clear of its path. The female had seen all this before, and her restlessness grew as the wind increased.

They lay in their shelter while the gale mounted steadily. Sand driven from the outer beaches flew like buckshot downwind and tore into their feathers, and the shelter behind the log began to fill up. It was clearly time to go—or be buried alive.

The sky had turned to a dirty yellow, and the roar of the wind mounted to an ear-piercing shriek. They could not tell rain from wind-driven spray now, and had to turn downwind before they could open their eyes. The female was the first to go; the second she spread her wings she was gone forever from his life. He followed a moment later, a mote of thistledown completely at the mercy of the hurricane.

In a second he was a helpless piece of flotsam driven before the blast. It was all he could manage to keep upright as he thundered downwind faster than he had ever flown before. He had no choice of direction—there was only one way he could go, and any deviation from the course of the gale left him tossed helplessly back into the stream. A great light glared in his eyes for a second and then was gone as he missed the top of a lighthouse by ten feet. The turbulence behind it tossed him end over end. The wind, lashing over the top of the maelstrom that was the surface of the sea, pulled the crests off the heaving waves and bore the spray away like buckshot. There was no hope of flying here, and the big male survived only because he was able to gain sufficient altitude to rise above the surface zone before he was blown over the open sea.

Hour after hour he flew on, and the hurricane finally veered out to sea leaving him in the decreasing winds on its edge. Exhaustion was close upon him now as gradually he gained control of his direction and once more could fly normally. His wings beat on automatically long after his mind had become numbed and stunned. For hours he had seen only occasional glimpses of the ground below or the roaring foam that was the surface of the sea. He had no idea where he was.

It was now eight hours since he had sprung from the sandbar to follow his mate, and in that time he had been blown four hundred miles to the northeast. As the clouds broke, he saw below him in the dismal grayness a great hook of land extending across his course, and with the last of his strength he landed thankfully in a marsh pond on the leeward side. He was on the north shore of Cape Cod, back in the winter home of the blacks from the Northeast.

For twenty-four hours he rested to recover from his ordeal. At last he was aroused from his stupor by the glimpse of a white-tipped red brush sliding silently behind a bush a few yards away. In two steps he slid into the water. The frustrated fox rose and watched as the duck paddled out into the pond and began feeding.

He never saw his mate from Chesapeake Bay again, so he spent the rest of the fall alone, avoiding the gunners in the now long familiar marshes of the coast. He was content to be alone for a time, prospecting each marsh until he found a place where the gunners did not go. There he would feed during the night, being careful to enter and leave the area only after dark. No one saw him using it, and its reputation for being duckless remained unblemished. He discovered a chain of such private sanctuaries along the coast, and as long as he was unmated he used them regularly.

But as winter advanced the breeding urge mounted in him, and he abandoned his solitary habits to join the throng again. His strapping size and aggressive manner found him another mate before long. Soon he was following close behind a veteran female, entering her third breeding season, who knew well where she would nest. When spring came she led the way north up the long reaches of the coast he knew so well.

As the hurricane clawed its way up the coast, ripping up wharves and jetties and smashing everything in its way, storm warnings went out ahead of it as far as Nova Scotia. When it turned out to sea, every ship in its path made all haste to get clear. One of these was a great tanker low in the water with every tank full, on her way to the hungry markets of Europe.

She lay two hundred and fifty miles southeast of Cape Sable, the southernmost tip of Nova Scotia, directly in the path of the hurricane. Her low midships was soon awash in the mounting seas. By nightfall her captain had radioed that he was in trouble. A giant sea had smashed his rudder, and he was wallowing helplessly beam-on to the huge waves that now washed solid green water across the tanker's midships. No ship could take this pounding long. When a barely discernible dawn broke, the captain saw great cracks appearing in his plating and he knew the end had come.

He ordered all hands aft and sent out his S.O.S. An hour later he reported that the ship was breaking up fast and that help must come soon—but he was never heard from again. No help could reach him in the vortex of the hurricane, and searchers found a mile-wide oil slick at his last position after the storm had passed. Another name was added to the long list at Lloyd's after the bell was tolled—with a grim note: "No survivors."

When the big black and his mate reached the Bay of Fundy islands that year, they lost themselves in the host gathered there before pressing on to the North. He had no idea where she was taking him, but she seemed in no hurry now, and inclined to linger among the islands and the seaweed-covered reefs that appeared from beneath the swirling waters at low tide. Fat mussels and snails were everywhere, and life was good. The honking geese and the brant joined them on the reefs, and the world of the water-fowl was complete and joyous. The courting parties whirled about, and mated pairs watched with the sedate smugness of those who had all that behind them.

One day the pair joined a flock of blacks circling about the islands of Passamaquoddy Bay. These birds seemed restless and ready for a long journey. They wheeled past the cormorant rookery on White Head Island and headed straight out to sea. They were on their way to their breed-ing grounds in Nova Scotia, and they would cross the mouth of the Bay of Fundy by the outermost islands of the New Brunswick shore.

As they were flying in fog partway across the Grand Manan Channel, a long low reef suddenly loomed ahead. They had seen no reef here on their other crossings, and the female set her wings to land nearby. The waves broke against it, but there was a strange smooth quality about its surface that seemed unnatural. They landed beside it and were about to go ashore when the strange reef began to move. Yards of it slid by, and then in the fog ahead a shattering booming blow sent the startled ducks leaping into the air. A great blue whale, a hundred feet long, was lying on the surface and moving slowly into the oncoming tide.

They flew across the Grand Manan Channel, slipping through the fog low over the waves, and soon they could hear the pounding of heavy surf on a rock-bound coast. At the first reefs seals popped up in the water and lay in the tide pools; murres and gulls were everywhere. The blacks circled to the east coast, which was more sheltered, and landed on a tideflat. Here, after eating greedily of the apparently endless supply of small snails and amphipods, they walked across the beach to the mouth of a stream that tumbled out of the forested slope. The fast water had not frozen, and they had a welcome chance to rid themselves of the sea salt. They bathed happily.

In this region another animal had been eliminated from their world. The rocky shores of the Maine coast and the Bay of Fundy had been home to the largest mink in the world. The sea mink had lived here with the blacks and geese, brant and old squaws, Labrador ducks and great auks, and each year as they passed through in spring and fall the mink had taken its toll.

The big red-brown mink, who had lived only along the shore in salt and brackish water areas, did not compete with his relative the common mink of the freshwater streams and lakes. His coarse, reddish pelt was not as valuable as that of the shorter-haired and darker common mink. But he was much larger, and the trappers and hunters of this coast had even developed a special way of hunting him that has never been used on any other mink—they hunted him with dogs.

The last of the sea minks had caught a black duck and

eaten the breast after drinking the blood. It lay relaxed on the seaweed atop a boulder when the sound of barking reached it from the shore of a large nearby island. The sound was still a long way off, but it appeared to be getting closer. The mink slid into the water with scarcely a ripple and made for the island where it lived, feeling full and lazy and thinking only of a long sleep in one of its familiar lying-up places on the shore. It moved at its looping walk up the beach to the cliff face behind and crawled deep into a long dry crevice above high-water mark. There it curled up and went to sleep.

The hunter following his dogs along the shore first noticed the down from the duck carcass on the reef beyond the beach. Some had blown to the shore, and he recognized it at once as from a black duck. He waded out to the reef and examined the carcass, and it took but a glance to tell him this was not the work of an eagle. He returned quickly to the beach. In his hand he carried some pungent mink droppings he found beside the carcass. He called to his dogs and rubbed their noses in the droppings and urged them on. They needed no more.

Soon they picked up the scent where the mink had left the water, and followed it to the entrance of the crevice. The mink awoke to the snuffling of noses and the whining of dogs trying frantically to dig him out of his rockbound fastness. His furious snarl only drove them to a frenzy of greater efforts.

When the hunter arrived he took a small crowbar from his pack and attempted to pry loose the rocks, but soon he too was forced to give up. Carefully he unloaded one barrel of his muzzle-loading shotgun and replaced the heavy shot with ground-up rock sulfur. ("Brimstone" was a standard part of his equipment.) Dragging the lead dog back, he thrust the muzzle as far into the crevice as he could, and fired.

The snarling mink had backed to the end of the crack and was facing the entrance with gleaming teeth bared when the twin black tubes poked into sight. The blast shattered his eardrums, but he was out of line of the charge, and lay stunned for a few seconds. The fumes of burning sulfur soon aroused him, choking. With his lips drawn back past the gums, and teeth bared for battle, he threw himself full on the dog's face that was blocking the entrance. Immediately he was buried under a swirling mass of snarling dogs. When he was dead the hunter had to pry his jaws loose from their grip on what was left of the lead dog's face. The other barrel put it out of its agony.

Thus died the last of the sea minks of the northeast coast. The year was 1894, just four years after the last passenger pigeon in eastern Canada was killed, twenty-three years after the last Labrador duck was taken in the Grand Manan Islands, and fifty years after the last of the great auks was clubbed to death. The black ducks feeding in the 'tween-tides seaweed were once again witness to the extinction of another member of their world.

After a week in the Fundy islands a string of blacks rose and headed out to sea. They flew just over the fog that blanketed the surface and kept the booming foghorns bellowing at regular intervals to the passing ships. At the Grand Manan Islands they stopped briefly and were joined by the pair. Soon the leader was off again. She swung out to sea, heading for Nova Scotia, and as they left the coast the fog disappeared and a bright sun broke through. In beautiful clear weather they dropped to a height just above the swells, and flew steadily eastward.

As they were closing the coast, the big male noticed several glassy patches that showed dark on the green sea's surface where no waves broke. They passed long lines of drifting seaweed, but these were different; from the air they looked like pools of brown glass.

The coastal reefs appeared ahead, and at the first the leader set her wings and glided down. The others followed in order until all were resting on the seaward side of the reef, riding the calm swells. Soon they spread out in pairs. Just to seaward one of the peculiar glassy patches rose and fell on the incoming seas.

The big male raised his head and looked in surprise at the oncoming wave. Its surface was dark brown, and its smooth, sluggish crest seemed to lift with difficulty. Drifting oil from the sunken tanker was washing ashore, and it meant death to thousands of seabirds. He watched innocently as it approached, curious, for it was beyond his experience, and when it reached him he sat quite still as the thick oily sludge closed around him. Then he felt the first stabs of chill into his belly as his feathers became saturated and lost their insulating properties. With a squawk of alarm he tried to rise, but when his wings touched the surface his primaries stuck together and he lost the power of flight. As he flopped back into the stinking pool he dived, made for the edge, and rose in the clean water beyond.

The other ducks looked at him in astonishment, as they could see no danger as he flopped toward the reef and dragged himself out. Though he preened frantically, he could not remove the sticky stuff from his primaries or his

breast, and in trying he swallowed quantities of it. He retched and vomited but he could not get rid of the oil, which, as it washed ashore, trapped the rest of the flock against the reef.

As the dark sludge washed up on the rocks, the seaweed became covered with it and the whole reef turned an oily black. A gull alighting on it skidded on its belly in landing, fouling its snow-white breast. Soon the chill penetrated to the bird's bone and it retired, cowering and shivering, to the lee of a boulder to begin the hopeless task of trying to preen itself clean.

Now birds of all sorts began to wash ashore. Dead and dying eiders and scoters; murres and puffins; gulls and terns; as well as ducks, geese, and brant, lined the shore. The killing chill of the water on their oil-drenched bodies drove those that could still crawl ashore, but the true sea-birds died in thousands. Horrified spectators came to look, and the local wildlife authorities broadcast an appeal for assistance to any who would come to the shore and help save the survivors. Washing stations were set up where living birds could be taken and their plumage cleaned. After they dried they were released on a clean shore, but even the most heroic efforts reached only a small portion of the birds affected. The coast became a charnelhouse marked by columns of black smoke where oil-soaked debris and dead birds were piled and burned.

The male had managed to reach shore just ahead of the edge of the oil, but his mate had swum directly into it, some of it splashing over her back. She was saturated beyond hope of recovery, and just managed to reach her mate on shore. They slipped and slid their way over the oily gravel, getting more soiled at every tumble, until they collapsed on the open beach.

At first light next morning the beach looked like a battlefield. The dead lay in windrows at the edge of the oily surf, and the living staggered and slithered among them, retching and vomiting an oily discharge. The female had died during the night, but the big male was still alive. She lay on her back, her saturated breast turned up to the chill wind, and he crouched beside her with his wings clasped to his sides, husbanding the last of his body heat.

131

He was only dimly conscious now, and the voice beside him evoked not the faintest stir:

"Here's a live one. He's pretty far gone, but we can try anyhow. Look! He's banded!"

A young man and a girl in hip rubber boots smeared with oil came slipping over the beach, picked him up gently, and placed him in a sack. The last thing he saw as the sack was closed and he was borne away was the body of his mate being raked into a pile of other bodies.

For a long time he learned very little. Several other oil-soaked birds joined him in the sack. At last they were gently lowered to the ground and he was carefully lifted out. He was too weak to stand, and he offered no resistance as he was swabbed down with a solution that slowly removed the oil from his feathers.

They offered him water, but he only vomited it back when he took it, so he closed his eyes and sank into a torpor. He and a dozen other black ducks were put in a crate. A farmer took them to his home and turned them loose on the side of his farm pond. Three were too far gone, and died that night, but by morning the big male was standing and had managed to hold down some clean fresh water. Cautiously he examined his plumage. Thanks to the cleaning solution, there was only the faintest trace of oil left, but his feathers were matted and out of place. He set to work preening himself all over, and by noon he was swimming about the pond, eating duckweed. At dusk he left.

His band number was recorded before he was turned loose, and in due course the circumstances of his recapture and release in Nova Scotia were added to his growing record in Washington and Ottawa.

He had had enough of the sea for a long time now, and

he wandered into the muskeg and lake country of the center of southern Nova Scotia. There, near Lake Rossignol, he watched the deer and the occasional moose come out to the lakes to feed as the aquatic plants developed. The calling of the frogs and the glorious full-throated laughter of the loons echoed across the silent lakes each evening.

All thought of mating that year had disappeared with the shambles of the oil tragedy, and he spent the early summer alone. A horned owl marked him down, but he was too old a hand to fall victim to local predators now. He took all the necessary precautions, and the owl soon gave up when it found it could not catch him off guard.

He was wandering through the muskegs where the bog cranberries grew in profusion each fall. The great flocks of Eskimo curlews had filled up on them here before starting their tremendous three-thousand-mile nonstop flight to the grassy llanos of the Venezuelan interior. These curved-billed waders had come in their thousands from their far-off breeding grounds on the barrens between the mouth of the Mackenzie and the Coppermine rivers. They crossed to southern Labrador and down to Nova Scotia before taking off to South America on one of the epic bird migrations of the world.

At least they *had* come. As the last of the sea minks was being hunted down on Campobello Island, the great flocks of curlews began to decline. The barrens where they nested were untouched, and the wastes of Labrador were the same. The cranberries for their final meal still grew in Nova Scotia, and the Atlantic storms were no fiercer or more frequent than they had ever been. The toll of the scattered local Indians and others in Venezuela was not known to have changed—yet the birds were obviously decreasing rapidly, just as had the passenger pigeon. The answer lay in the spring flight.

In spring the great flocks crossed the Gulf of Mexico to the Texas coast to begin their long overland journey to the arctic barrens. Here their numbers reminded the American settlers of the clouds of passenger pigeons they had until very recently known farther east. They even called them the "prairie pigeon," and the similarity did not end there. So tame were the curlews, and so used to traveling in their massed flocks, that they were the easiest of all birds to shoot. Again the gunners turned out en masse. The slaughter soon rivaled that of the passenger pigeon, and the curlews were hauled to market by the wagonload. In the hot spring sun many spoiled before arrival; when that happened the whole load was simply dumped on the prairie and the gunner refilled his wagon from the still circling flocks. Pump guns were now available, and one hunter claimed to have killed thirty-seven birds from a rising flock with one of these new guns. As they carried at least five shells, they were obviously the answer for the market hunter.

Soon the massed migration was gone. The spring flight over the great plains dwindled to small flocks that were not worth the gunners' time, and the curlews disappeared from the market. Unlike the passenger pigeon, their nesting grounds were unaltered; there was still hope for the species as long as it had not been forced beyond the point of no return as had the Labrador duck. But each year the flocks grew smaller. In the last thirty-two years the species has been seen only eleven times—six times on the coast of Texas and five times on the Atlantic coast. The whistle of the curlew became an unknown sound to the young black ducks finishing their first summer in the muskeg ponds of Nova Scotia. And so it had been ever since as the big male spent his solitary year recovering from his ordeal by oil in their solitudes.

About the time the great flocks of curlews began to decrease, another animal disappeared forever from the muskegs, barrens, and forests of Nova Scotia and New Brunswick. The long, mournful howl of the timber wolf that rose to a frozen sky as the aurora danced in the heavens was heard no more. The big gray wolves could not be tolerated around the settlements, and as they competed with man for the moose, caribou, and deer, a no-quarter war was waged against them. The black ducks on their forest lakes had watched the wolves padding along the beaches and swimming the rivers in their endless wanderings. To the ducks the wolf was another inhabitant of their world that they treated with respect but no particular fear, as the wolf did not molest them. When they were gone, this part of the world was again one species poorer; they would not meet wolves again south of the St. Lawrence.

As the big male flew across the muskeg to his favorite feeding lake, he crossed trails worn deep into the bog plants by many cloven hooves. These were caribou trails that showed the wanderings of generations of animals that now were no more. When the settlers moved into the back country of Nova Scotia, wild game was their principal meat supply. Of these the caribou was the easiest to kill. Least able to tolerate the approach of settlements, caribou retreated as far into the interior as they could go. But nowhere were they beyond the reach of the meat hunters in this sea-girt province. Today all that remains are their well-worn trails, slowly healing with the years, across the mossy barrens where the stags pursued the does during the autumn rut a mote of time ago.

The big male molted alone that summer, and when he could fly he wandered northward. He was slowing down now, and the old violent urges were not so strong. He crossed the province to Minas Basin, but because he found little to his liking on the red mud shores and the miles of tideflats exposed at each low tide, he crossed to the New Brunswick coast. There he found others of his kind that satisfied such need for company as he felt, and he joined them gratefully in their salt-marsh pools.

As fall progressed he lingered along the Bay of Fundy shore, moving generally in a southwesterly direction from feeding ground to feeding ground. There, on the cold, spray-swept ledges, he felt safe from man. The blacks joined the eiders and scoters and flew in long strings between the islands.

But even there he was not completely safe. The band he was with rose one day to pass over a herring weir with its gull-topped posts. A flock of huge black ducks appeared ahead, clustered about a rocky seaweed-draped ledge. His companions had never seen black ducks of such size before, and immediately set course to join them. If these magnificent strangers were safe here, surely black ducks half their size must be safe too, and they came straight in with none of the customary circling. As the leader's big red feet reached for the water, a forest of splashes rose around him and a shotgun boomed from the rockpile on the ledge. The big male fled headlong, but none of the giant newcomers followed him; they remained quietly bobbing on the swells beside the innocent-looking ledge. He had encountered his first set of outsized decoys used by the sea duck hunters of the New England coast. He would not again approach these large and conspicuous black ducks that he could see at twice the normal distance. He had added another trick to his store of survival lore.

In the shortening days of December he drifted south as the cold sealed off the northern coast. He found it less to his liking each year now, and he did not stop until he reached the southern coast of New Jersey, where he settled thankfully into winter quarters south of the permanent snow.

Part 3

Chapter Twelve

Spring found him once again threading his way up the coast in the wake of a new-found mate. One morning the tinkling of breaking shell ice aroused him as he dozed in the bright March sun. The strident calling of a ring-billed gull overhead brought him back to his position on the shore of a tide pool on Grand Manan Island. His newly won mate was nearby, and they began a lazy circle of the pool. She led as usual, and as the tide rose they left the pool and swam across a strip of deep water to an offshore islet.

The islet, crowned with wind-blown spruces, was barely an acre in extent, without fresh water. They had hardly reached the shore before a brown body scurried over the seaweed and disappeared up the bank on a well-used trail. Wherever they went on the islet these trails crisscrossed, and their makers, always busy muskrats, watched them at every turn. Why these animals of the freshwater marshes and streams should colonize an islet off a large island separated from the mainland by fifteen miles of open sea is a mystery that naturalists have not solved.

There was a full moon that night as they joined a long, straggling flock of ducks moving northeast. They were following a large flock of Canada geese that were beating steadily into the gloom ahead over the white landscape below. After two hours' flying they came to a great river with large patches of open water showing between the ice pans. Here the whole company landed to feed and rest.

They had reached the estuary of the St. John River, in New Brunswick. When they arrived they found numbers of black-and-white goldeneye drakes bobbing before their hens. These divers throve in the open water between the running ice, but it was too deep for the geese and blacks to feed. After an hour's rest the geese lifted again and headed upriver, followed by a long line of paired blacks.

Where the Jemseg River drains the mighty complex of lakes and marshes that are its watershed into the St. John the geese for many years have used a pasture on a southern exposure as a feeding and resting area as soon as it becomes clear of snow. Today it is a farm on the edge of a marsh, but they still came each spring. The goose flock landed with the blacks, sliding into the open water of the main river nearby. Here they would tarry a month on their northward flight, and many blacks would go no farther as the vast maze of swamps, creeks, leads, and marshes surrounding the hillside was their summer home.

The first week in April found the big male setting his wings to glide down to the open water below the goose pasture at Jemseg behind his new mate. The courting parties of goldeneyes dotted the open water between the ice pans, but the hillside was already bare and the soft gabble of contented geese rose from the feeding multitude.

That evening, as he and his mate were feeding up one of the many open channels in the marsh, a muskrat plunged into the water ahead and swam toward them. The furry rodent showed no interest as they pased. There was no fresh vegetation showing yet, so they fed in the belt of seeds along the edge of the rising flood. Here all of last year's crop was well represented; they could pick and choose.

As they approached a point jutting out into the lake, the ever-alert male saw a canoe with two men in it approaching. He herded his mate into the shelter of a large block of stranded ice and watched carefully as the canoe came near and turned into the channel they had just left. Beyond the point where they had passed the muskrat the canoe stopped, and the man in the bow leaned over and pulled toward him a log floating in the channel. He swung his paddle under it, and some wet chain glistened in the sun. Hand over hand he pulled in the muskrat, which was held firmly by a hind leg in the trap attached to the end of the chain. He dropped the drowned rat into the bottom of the canoe and reset the trap. Then he carefully placed it in a notch specially cut in the log where it lay with its open jaws just below the surface.

As they paddled on around the lake, checking their trapline, the pile of muskrat carcasses grew apace in the bottom of the canoe. Each trap was carefully reset in a notch in a floating log. At the end of the day the men had checked

143

a hundred traps and had taken about seventy-five dollars' worth of muskrat pelts. As a special bonus they had caught a mink. They returned tired but satisfied to their trapping camp on the intervale, ready for the long evening job of skinning and stretching pelts. As they lighted their lantern, the pair of blacks slid over the camp and settled in the channel behind.

The female was ready to nest, and he followed as she investigated each likely place. However she could find no site that would be above the rising flood. She knew this by some subtle instinct her forefathers had developed through generations of nesting and rearing their broods in this treacherous flood country. The big male watched with amazement when his mate began flying up into trees to examine cavities and crotches like a wood duck or a goldeneye. None of his other mates had ever done this, and it was something new to him.

The wooded creeks and swamps stretched for miles, and she took her time making her selection. Finally she settled on an old stag-headed silver maple from which several large branches had broken off. Here she found what she sought —the hollow stub of a limb down which she could drop to a dry chamber lined with punk and bark. This she immediately began to fill with the dark-colored down plucked from her breast. The big male established his territory on a section of a nearby channel as a white-throated sparrow's "Sweet . . . sweet . . . sweet . . . sweet . . . Canada . . . Canada . . . Canada" rose from the alders, and a flicker clacked incessantly from a nearby stub.

The first day he was there the trappers came through his channel; he left hurriedly as they entered his territory. He had found a fine loafing spot on a floating log, but having seen the men in plenty of time, he flushed while they were still a hundred yards away. As the canoe came abreast of his log, the bowman pointed silently to it and reached for a trap as they came alongside.

Two expert blows of the ax sent a large chip flying, and a staple secured the end of the trap chain to the side of the log. The set trap just covered the fresh notch, and the water lapped gently through it. The trappers retrieved the chip, flung it off up the bank, and continued on their way.

They had hardly rounded the bend before the big black was back in his territory. Soon the female joined him and they fed quietly along the channel. When they were full she returned to her nest building, and he, lazy and contented, swam back to his loafing log. As he approached he unconsciously swam to the lowest point where it would be easiest to climb out.

As he turned in to the notch, his first step went squarely into the trap. The jaws closed over his leg with a numbing shock as he plunged frantically off the log. In the water the weight of the trap and the chain suspended from his leg dragged him down so that it was all he could do to keep his head above water. With his first wild lunge he felt the bone in his leg snap.

For the first half hour he fought silently but furiously with all his strength against this thing that held him captive, despite the searing pain that every movement caused in his broken leg. After this the unrelenting grip of the trap made his whole leg numb, and he was spared the initial agony. As hour after hour went by, his strength waned, and his mate found him resting his tired head on the log. She could not understand what was wrong with him. The trap was out of sight under water, and her great mate lay more dead than alive, resting his chin on a fresh-cut notch in the log. Bewildered, she returned to her nest.

He was still alive the next morning as the canoe rounded the bend. His only defense as the trappers came alongside was to sink even lower in the water. The bowman hauled him in unceremoniously, but as they lifted him into the canoe he had enough strength left to splash water over them.

"There'll be no rat here for us today—but I guess we got our dinner anyway. His leg's broke, so I might as well knock him on the head."

"Wait a minute! He's banded. Look—on the other leg!"

"Sure enough! Must belong to somebody. Better let him go. We don't want the wardens getting too nosy around here. Pass the knife."

Long ago he had lost all feeling in the shattered leg gripped by the trap, and he felt nothing as the knife severed the tendons at the break. The trap, still holding his leg, fell away from him.

At first he did not realize he was free, and just lay on the water, feeling its icy bite on his severed stump. Then, with a few flaps of his saturated wings, he was across the channel and into the brush. He lay there long after the sounds of the canoe had faded in the distance.

For centuries some of the black ducks of the Grand Lake area had moved out of the great marshes each summer into an area of ponds and barrens that lay about ten miles to the north. Here in this inaccessible region where the only human intruder was an occasional forester, they gathered in almost complete isolation. This area, called the Bull Pasture Plains because of the rutting bull moose that met there each fall in fierce combat, was once the home of a herd of woodland caribou. These solitude-loving animals had frequented this isolated barren for many years, and

147

their trenchlike trails were worn deeply into the moss. Here the Maliseet hunters, the native Indians of the St. John River, had watched the clouds of black ducks that rose before them as they pushed out through the ponds in search of a moose or a caribou.

Later the camp hunters of the lumber industry, and the settler in search of his winter meat, reached the edge of the barren and saw the white rumps of the caribou fading into the timber on the far side. Now a few daintily stepping deer were to be seen about the edge of the barren, and the caribou were fewer. The local ducks still came each summer to molt, and the migrant geese each fall when the cranberries were ripe.

The great white-maned caribou stags still followed the crisscrossed trails over the barren in pursuit of the does, but each year the long wail of a cow moose and the answering grunt of the bull became more common in the October dusk. The moose eruption was under way, but the caribou were doomed. The last survivors set off at their swinging trot, heading north in single file, and they were seen no more on the barren. The black ducks poured in from the lake as usual that fall and listened to the clash of moose antlers, but where once the caribou had grazed on the moss now a great buck defended his doe and ran hot and panting to the pond to slake his thirst. The cranberry-filled ducks swam aside to make room for him, but none bothered to fly.

This sanctuary in the deep forest was to play a part in the life of the big male black, now crouching terrified and in pain in the brush beside the channel. The shock of his injury removed all the usual instincts but that of simple survival, and he never returned to his territory. However,

148

he soon learned to take off from both land and water on his one leg, and within a week he had almost forgotten that he once had two feet—so little did his loss incapacitate him.

His accident had cut short his breeding-season activities, and he found himself one of the first to arrive at the male concentration areas in preparation for his molt. While waiting for others to complete their family duties and join him, he wandered about the maze of lakes and marshes, timbered swamps and secluded beaver ponds that forms the duck breeding grounds of central New Brunswick. He saw the great gaunt cow moose bringing their small brown calves to the marshes for their first introduction to succulent aquatic plants, and he watched the deer shedding into their red summer coats. An osprey screamed overhead and cast a baleful eye upward at the white flashes of a bald eagle's head and tail showing against the June sky. Life was vibrant and noisy all about after the warbler migration arrived from the South, and a bittern boomed from the edge of the flood. The black-and-scarlet jewel that was a redstart darted through the alders. A cedar waxwing flirted his golden-tipped tail and turned his crested black-masked head to watch as the big black landed in a pond.

He was soon joined by several other males who one day led him off to the north, leaving the lakes and marshes behind. He followed as they climbed over the timbered slope stretching away in unbroken forest to the horizon, but soon a break in the vast canopy appeared on the skyline. A great patch of brown bog dotted with ponds came into view, and as the Bull Pasture Plains slid below they banked and sideslipped into the largest of the ponds.

Deer wandered sedately about, and a great blue heron

149

fished for frogs in the next pond, but there was no sign of man or his works. The cranberries of the fall were not yet grown, but the foods of the bog ponds he had known so well in the North were all about him. That evening a dozen more male blacks arrived, and within a few days they numbered a score or more scattered over the bog. As this was the ideal place for them to pass their flightless period, the edges of the ponds were soon lined with shed feathers.

Though he did not know it, the short flight from Grand Lake to the Bull Pasture Plains was to be one of the most momentous of his life. He had entered the Kingdom of the Caterpillar.

Chapter Thirteen

Between the lower St. Lawrence and the Bay of Fundy lies a great area of forested hills and winding rivers that is called the Acadian Forest Region. Here trees grow faster than anywhere else in eastern Canada. And it is here also that a small brown caterpillar less than an inch long has, with the help of man, become master of the destiny of the birds, animals, fish, and other lesser creatures that live in these great forests. This curious fact has placed the men who have to make the decisions on forest policy on the horns of a deadly dilemma.

It all began thousands of years ago, before the coming of the white man, when the small brown caterpillar, the spruce budworm, crawled to the tip of the branch of a fir tree and began systematically to strip it of needles.

When enough needles were eaten the old trees died; as they were blown down openings appeared in the vast forest. In these openings the new growth provided winter browse for moose and deer, and when lightning struck the blowdowns great areas of the country burned. On these burns the caribou grazed on the lichens while the grouse and woodcock frequented the forest edge and the green alder runs along the streams that were too wet to burn. The ducks and geese were unaffected.

Then came the white man, and the forest became an enemy to be defeated by any means available. The great budworm outbreaks and the fires that followed them were welcomed by the settlers as the only means of removing the all-pervading forest on a large scale. Wood was everywhere and had no commercial value, and hunting and fishing for sport had hardly begun.

In the great sea battles of the Napoleonic Wars Britain's sea supremacy was born, and with it a demand for tall straight masts and spars for the Royal Navy that no longer could be filled in Scandinavia. To meet this demand men followed all the rivers of the Acadian Forest to carve the broad arrow of the Royal Navy on the trunks of selected tall pines. The lumber trade was born. Now, for the first time, wood had real value, and the forest industries of eastern Canada had their beginnings.

Towns grew up dependent almost entirely on the lumber trade for their support. The country developed, with the forest industries bearing the largest share of the costs. Wood had become King, surpassing by far fishing, mining, and even agriculture. And still the small brown caterpillar gnawed away at the needles in the tops of the spruce and

152

The winter range from southern Nova Scotia to Chesa-peake Bay

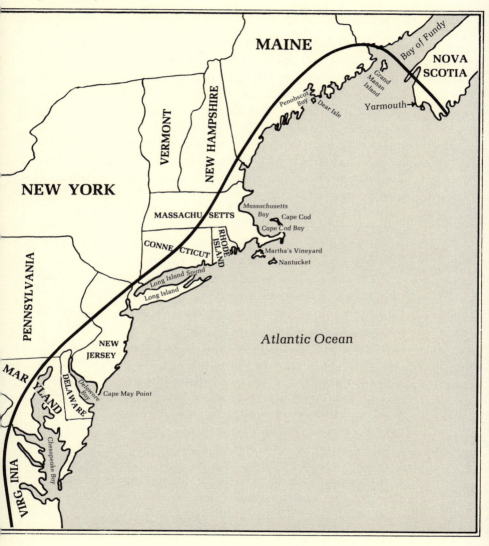

fir. Periodically they burst forth in their millions, and large numbers of spruce and fir trees died in their wake. But the outbreak would run its course and die out, and new growth would replace the trees killed.

The lumber industry dealt only in mature trees, and the taller and thicker the better. Soon the mature forest began to disappear, its place taken by second-growth forests of smaller size. As the human population of the continent grew, chains of newspapers developed in all the large centers and the demand for more and more paper began to be heard. This was a lifesaver to the forest industries of eastern Canada, as many lumber operations had been forced to close when they ran out of mature timber. The timberlands were now covered with small trees just beginning to reach maturity—small trees just the right size for pulpwood to make paper. And so was born the pulp and paper industry that is the greatest source of revenue in the Acadian Forest today. But still the small brown caterpillars were chewing away in the crowns of the trees.

With the change from long lumber to pulpwood, the importance of the small brown caterpillar greatly increased. Pulpwood limits are managed on as short a rotation as possible; hence the extremely rapid rate of growth in the Acadian Forest made it the ideal place for such operations. The mills were sited at the mouths of the rivers, and the watersheds were divided into cutting units to be harvested in rotation for many years ahead. A budworm outbreak now would seriously disrupt this schedule, and might well necessitate the closing of the whole operation, with economic disaster to the community it supported.

Foresters then began to view the small brown caterpillar with considerable apprehension, and hot spots of infestation were carefully noted. Then, in 1951, the alarm was

154

sounded. A population of budworms in northern New Brunswick was on the verge of breaking out into a full-scale eruption again, and the limits of a large pulp mill were threatened. All other companies with limits in the area were also endangered, and meetings were held between the pulp and paper industry and the provincial and federal forestry officials. It was decided that something must be done to head off the impending disaster.

Now spruce and fir trees, budworms, animals, birds, and fish had all lived together in the Acadian Forest for eons and had worked out their own checks and balances over the centuries. If budworms could ever have turned the region into a desert, they would have done so long before the first white man saw it. But something new had now been added. Man had invented new chemical poisons, hitherto completely unknown in nature, and an instrument for spreading them on a broad scale over the landscape was at hand. The two weapons chosen for the defense against the latest budworm outbreak were DDT and the airplane.

By 1952 the opposing forces were on the field, and battle was joined. Airfields were hewn from the forest, and professional spray pilots were recruited from all over the continent to deliver the poison. The roar of the low-flying planes was heard for the first time over the watershed of the Upsalquitch, a tributary of the famous Restigouche, where about 300 square miles were sprayed. But this was but a small part of the outbreak, and plans were made for a greatly expanded effort the following spring.

During the winter of 1952–1953, more airfields were constructed and stocked with poison, and when the planes arrived that spring the greatest onslaught against the spruce budworm ever mounted began to roll. When the last plane switched off its engine, 2,800 square miles had been sprayed, and optimistic forecasts were made for an early victory in the Battle of the Budworm. But the area under moderate to severe attack now extended from Gaspé almost to Nova Scotia, and a new outbreak had been spotted down on the shores of the Bay of Fundy. The small brown caterpillar was not to be counted out yet.

In 1954 another 1,800 square miles were sprayed, all in the north of the province. The following year yet another 1,800 square miles were sprayed, mostly in the areas sprayed before. By 1956 an all-out effort was made, and 3,100 square miles, some resprayed and some new territory, were sprayed. Still the caterpillars extended the range of infestation, reaching Grand Lake and crossing the St. John River at Fredericton. Worried looks appeared on the faces of public officials when the bills, now well into the millions of dollars, began to come in. They were so deeply committed now that there was no alternative to pressing on to what they hoped would prove a final victory. But the budworm continued to extend its range.

By 1957 it was decided to pull out all the stops, and the mightiest air fleet ever assembled in the battle covered 8,100 square miles with poison. But that year the caterpillars reached the head of the Belle Isle in southern New Brunswick, and Charlotte County in the extreme Southwest. They had spread 160 miles southwest from their original location on the upper Upsalquitch to Charlotte County in just five years, despite the best efforts of the sprayers and the expenditure of millions of dollars to stop them.

By 1958 the outbreak had passed its peak, and the southern edge, which had never been sprayed, began to draw back. However, in the North it flared up again, and 4,100 square miles, most of it respray, were treated that year. By this time a total of 22,000 square miles had been sprayed, parts of it as many as five times, and the costs approached $10 million. There was no longer any loose talk about quelling the outbreak, and somber questions about "keeping the trees alive" were being heard. The talk was now all about minimizing the damage until the outbreak ran its course. No one was under any delusions any longer about "putting out the fire."

By 1959, seven years from the start of the outbreak, things had quieted down considerably, and the sprayers held their fire—and their breath. However, that summer was a successful breeding season for budworms, and by 1960 the sprayers were out again in force, and 4,070 square miles were sprayed that spring. In 1961 the outbreak showed signs of dying down again, but 2,810 square miles were sprayed as a precaution. The spring of 1962 called for a further 3,100 square miles of spraying. Between 1952 and 1963 a total of 9,695,000 pounds of DDT was sprayed on 11,615,000 acres of forest, streams, and lakes, and no end was yet in sight. By 1964 the cost passed $18 million. The budworm is still there, and fully capable of bursting out again in destructive numbers in its own good time.

The biologist sat hot, tired, and dusty, with his nose in the foam of a mug of beer. He had been counting grouse broods all day along survey lines in the forest, and the numbers he found had been disappointingly small. He hardly looked up as a stranger slid into the chair opposite him.

"Barman said you were a wildlife biologist. Mind if I ask some questions?"

"Not a bit. Go right ahead."

"Well, I'm from Massachusetts and I've been coming up here for the past few years to get some early fishing. I'd heard about this budworm spraying that's been going on all these years, but it was always somewhere else. This year we got it. Fished five days and never got even a trout. How long you fellows going to keep this up?"

"The forestry people tell us there is no end in sight yet, and they call the shots around here."

"But surely you must be poisoning just about everything in the woods?"

"I reckon we have. And the biologists have not been backward in pointing it out either, but fish and wildlife are small beer here beside the pulp and paper industry. Until someone comes up with a way of controlling budworms and nothing else, or the industry learns to live with them as they do everywhere else, all we can do is bite our nails and take it."

"Is the budworm truly that destructive? Can it really wipe out the forest, as all this propaganda we hear would lead us to believe?"

"The first white men to see this country called it the great Acadian *forest,* not the great Acadian *desert,* and there had been budworms here for thousands of years. No, they do not destroy the forest. All they do is kill one generation of two kinds of trees—spruce and fir. Fires in the blowdowns may of course destroy other species too, but the budworms eat only those two."

"To justify spraying these vast areas and millions of trees, each and every one must be harvested or it will only die of old age anyway. Do you expect to be able to do that?"

"There's not a chance. The spray boys tell us they cannot leave unsprayed pockets behind to reinfest the sprayed area, so they spray everything."

"But do they get 100 percent kill? Surely there must be some left in the spray area to carry on, or this would have been all over long ago."

"They never get them all. There are always plenty left to produce the next generation. To my eyes it's like putting in a bounty hunter to clean out coyotes and then have him turn loose all the pregnant females. You can stay in the bounty business that way a long time."

"But surely the cost will put an end to this sooner or later. How much has this cost already?"

"The latest figure I saw was over $18 million. And that is only the cost of putting the poison on the ground. It does not include damage to wildlife, damage to fishing both commercial and sport, and damage to public health. You cannot put a dollar sign on any of these yet, but someday we will; and I think that when we do, the cost of putting out the poison will be only a small part of the bill."

"You're not very cheerful, are you?"

"How can you expect me to be? My whole life is wrapped up in fostering the welfare of the wildlife of this region; then along comes a monolithic thing like this from which there is no escape and no appeal. If you are in the way you get it whether you want it or not."

"When will it end?"

"When either the budworm supply or the money supply runs out. Which will give out first is anybody's guess."

"Well, thanks for the information anyway. I guess I'll try Nova Scotia for my spring fishing next year."

A clutch of salmon eggs hatched in the gravel of one of the small tributaries of the Miramichi River in New Brunswick. The tiny fry settled into the crannies between the pebbles to consume their yolk sacs. When these were gone they began their first short searches for food, and their development into small active fish really began. That day a plane roared low over the headwaters of the stream, trailing a long tail of mist behind it. This mist was DDT dissolved in solvent oil, and it settled on the foliage of the trees and killed most of the budworms feeding there. But the poisonous mist also settled indiscriminately on both land and water, and that night a rain shower washed more off the trees and into the stream.

The salmon fry were now feeding actively on tiny organisms on the stream bed. The day after the plane passed, those feeding farthest upstream felt a strange sensation in their gills. Thick mucus formed on the delicate membranes, and within five minutes the DDT had penetrated all their vital organs. Within five hours they were all dead except a few survivors who were lucky enough to stay in a back eddy where the poison did not reach.

When the survivors finally emerged into the main stream again they entered a world very different from what they had left. Where were the waving tails of the tiny fishlings foraging steadily in the cracks between the stones? And where was the multitude of tiny organisms on which they fed? Both were dead and washed away, and the survivors were hard pressed to find enough to eat, even with the whole stream bed to themselves.

Young salmon in this river grow and develop in freshwater for three summers. At the beginning of the fourth they put to sea. The survivors of the fry hatched that year all contained some DDT, as everything on which they fed carried it in small quantities. But it never reached the lethal level, and they continued to grow and develop into the smolt stage. As in all animal populations, there were some individuals more resistant to the poison than others, and these became the greater part of the population as the less resistant ones dropped out.

The same thing was happening among the surviving budworms in the crowns of the trees along the stream. The resistant and the lucky survived to breed the next generation—but a great difference had arisen between the situation the young salmon faced and that of the next generation of budworms. In the world of the salmon the survivors had to subsist on a greatly depleted food supply, but in the budworm's world the food supply was unlimited. In this utopia their numbers multiplied at the maximum rate, and in two years they were back to outbreak proportions again. The timber owner watched the crowns of the softwoods beginning to turn brown again as the needles disappeared, and that year the planes came back.

The surviving salmon fry were smolts now and much more resistant to the poison than they were the first time. They were also the resistant survivors of the first poisoning. This time when the deadly mist floated down on them some died, as did thousands of the newly hatched fry of the year, but the rest survived the new flood of poisoned water and the destruction of their food supply to go at last to the sea.

They would spend their period there eating mightily and growing into the sleek silver fighters that would return to their native river to spawn and continue their race when they had attained their full growth. But when that time came, instead of the great horde pressing up the river home from all parts of the far-flung waters of the Gulf and North Atlantic, there was but a pitiful handful left.

A French Canadian fisherman on the North Shore of the

Gulf of St. Lawrence hauled his nets and dumped the silver booty into the bottom of his boat. Back at the village his dark-eyed wife chattered happily to the children as the beautiful salmon he had brought home was cooking for supper. The next of the numerous brood stirred within her as she served supper, and into each and all of them that night went some of the poison the planes had loosed over the far-off Miramichi.

A Newfoundlander's dory grounded on the pebbly beach, and the prize of his catch that he bore home proudly contained its quota of poison to be passed on to his family. More of it was eaten by hardy Nova Scotia fisherfolk, and quite a lot went packed in ice to wealthy homes in the United States.

At Godthaab on the west coast of Greenland, fifteen hundred miles to the northeast, a fat Eskimo boy licked the grease off his fingers as he finished his meal, thus adding the poison of Miramichi to his body fat. A "livier" (a permanent resident of the coast of Labrador) did the same on his rockbound shore seven hundred miles to the west. In this manner the blight of the planes of Miramichi was spread.

The poison is spread more widely by the migrations of the salmon, but as they do most of their growing in the sea it is in low concentration by the time they reach full size. In the local trout, however, who grow all their lives in the poisoned waters and are subjected to annual doses, it steadily accumulates.

Today we know that DDT has infiltrated the food chains of the sea to such vast distances that even the eggs of antarctic penquins are hatched contaminated.

A woodcock sat toasting pleasantly in the warm May sun beside a clump of wire birch on a hillside overlooking the

Miramichi. She sat on her clutch of four mottled eggs, and only her eyes blinked from time to time to betray her perfectly camouflaged presence. Her mate had established his singing ground in the corner of a nearby field where he performed each morning and evening. Both he and his mate had arrived back on their breeding grounds that spring carrying in their bodies the poison heptachlor epoxide, or HE. This they had picked up after it had been liberally spread to kill fire ants in their winter range in the Deep South.

When the four eggs came, the female woodcock passed on to each a part of the HE she carried in her body, and the unborn chicks were poisoned before they even entered the world. When they were a few days old, the roaring planes passed over and the oily spray sifted down, covering everything around them. Their young bills were still too soft for probing as deeply as their mother could. They found the insects for their food under the leaves and among the vegetation on the surface. Before they were two weeks old they had added DDT to the HE passed on to them as a legacy from their mother.

As summer progressed, the DDT leached into the soil, where it was accumulated by the burrowing earthworms. When the beaks of the young woodcocks hardened, they followed their mother's example and began probing for earthworms. Soon they were consuming fifty or more each day, and they lived on little else. By the end of the summer they had all accumulated sizable amounts of DDT in their bodies.

When the leaves turned gold and crimson that fall, and the hunters and their belled dogs took to the field to harvest the annual crop of woodcock, the birds massed in their fall covers preparing to go south. They stuffed themselves with earthworms and laid on layer after layer of migration

163

fat as fuel for their long journey. As the first migrants left and the long trek began, hunter after hunter sat at table with his appetite keen for the rare delicacy his skill had provided. And thus was spread from New Brunswick to Louisiana the fruits of the small brown caterpillar of the great Acadian Forest, just as the fruits of the fire ants of the southern states were carried to New Brunswick by the returning birds in the spring.

This two-way traffic in man-made poisons by the unconscious birds is known to take place in the woodcock, and it probably takes place in other migratory birds, such as robins, with similar feeding habits. Game birds, however, and in this case the woodcock, are the only species that come into man's possession in sufficient numbers to make it possible to find out. How many more poison carriers there are that cover thousands of miles with no regard for political boundaries is not known, but that they are many seems certain.

Young ducks hatched on the shores of the Arctic Ocean a thousand miles north of any known source of DDT have been found to be carrying the poison. It must have come from their mothers, who migrate to the DDT areas for the winter. It is finally deposited in the bodies of the arctic peoples, who have never known the poison but who eat ducks as their southern neighbors do.

The hen grouse shepherding her brood through the June woods looked up at the roaring planes passing overhead with the long oily trails of mist floating down. She and her chicks gobbled up the dying insects that fell from the trees.

A doe with her twin fawns darted for cover as the low-flying planes passed, but quickly resumed browsing on the new green foliage even as the spray settled on it.

A bald eagle found the fish floating belly up in a pond

very much to his taste despite the oily scum on the surface, and bore them to his two young in the great nest a mile away.

Even the she bear picked it up as she showed her cubs that certain vegetation was very satisfying food when it was young and succulent in early summer.

And, despite all the planes could do, the small brown caterpillars continued to chew away on the balsam needles. Millions died each spring, but millions more survived. The annual reduction caused by the spray assured an ample food supply for the survivors, and their sturdy offsprings were becoming more and more tolerant of their annual shower of poison. Thus, after thirteen years, the program became almost self-perpetuating. Meanwhile, the residues piled up in almost all wildlife below.

It was into this Kingdom of the Caterpillar that the big male flew as he settled on a pond in the spruce-rimmed bog of the Bull Pasture Plains.

Chapter Fourteen

The big male had been flightless for about a week when the sound of a plane approaching brought him to full attention. It skimmed low over the bog, and just as it passed over him and rose over the timber behind a cloud of midst burst out in a long trail. The spray widened and slowly sank to the trees and the ground beneath. Some of it fell to the surface of the pond and left an oily scum on the smooth water. The annual spraying of the forests of New Brunswick had begun; each day for a week the spray planes covered the surrounding forest, and each day the brooks brought more of the oily scum into the bog ponds.

The male black was spending his flightless period in a

pond fed by a brook draining the sprayed forest. On the second day of spraying an afternoon rain shower brought a quantity of the oily material down the brook. The next morning he paddled with his one leg along the shore. He had not gone far before he came to insects floating dead on the surface. These were a welcome addition to his diet, so he gobbled up all he could find. After the planes went away, insects of any kind were scarce, and he found difficulty in finding the aquatic kinds he sought regularly as food. Those he found were dead, but he ate them just the same. Thus did he acquire his first dose of pesticide poison. It settled in his brain, his heart, his fat, and his reproductive organs.

At the same time, far to the south, as the mayor of a seashore resort opened his mail a frown deepened on his face. It contained numbers of complaints from real-estate dealers and private individuals that they either could not sell property or were selling out at a loss and moving away. The reason was that mosquitoes from the great salt marshes behind the beach were making life unbearable outdoors.

It did not take the mayor long to call his sanitary engineer and the Health Department, and very soon a contract was let to spray the marshes for mosquito control. As the planes swept over the New Brunswick forests far to the north, killing budworms by the millions, bringing short-lived joy to the hearts of foresters who knew they would be back again next year, similar planes were crisscrossing the marshes where the ducks wintered, trailing swaths of deadly spray behind them. Because this was to be a concentrated effort to get rid of the pests once for all, the dosage was much higher than it was in the North.

As it settled, the mosquitoes and their wriggling larvae

died in millions, but so also did many other creatures. DDT is no respecter of species, and all insects, including those that ate mosquitoes or their larvae, were killed indiscriminantly. Their bodies fell into the water. The small fish gobbled up this windfall until they could hold no more —then they too turned belly up and died. The clams and mussels accumulated the residue, and all the lesser forms of life down to the smallest plankton, the basis of all aquatic life, felt its weight.

An osprey paused in its flight across the marsh, poising over a channel on beating wings. With a forward tilt it plunged to the surface and rose with a dead fish in its talons. He carried it to his mate on the heap of dead sticks in the tall stub that was their nest and watched as she tore it up to feed it to the chicks.

He was returning within a few minutes with a second of the fish that were appearing all over the area when he saw his only enemy. As a bald eagle swooped from above, he screamed defiance and took immediate evasive action. But the eagle was not interested in him or his prize, and continued on to the water to pick up a fish of its own. Its mate had already carried all the fledglings could eat to the nest that day.

A great blue heron stalked majestically about the flats, picking up frogs and crayfish, dead fish and salamanders, until it could hold no more. The shore-feeding raccoons were soon glutted with dead fish too, as were the scavenger crows and the gulls; before the summer was over the insidious poison that had been sprayed over the marsh to kill mosquitoes infiltrated almost every living thing in the vast community of life the marsh supported. Some would die like the mosquitoes, but most would live on, sterilized, or producing weak and deformed young that might not

live, depending upon how much of the poison they had acquired. The cottagers got their mosquito-free summer, but the life of the marsh paid a harsh price, and the poison would still be there, as deadly as ever, when the myriads of ducks, geese, and shorebirds arrived to spend the winter.

Back in the Grand Lake swamps of New Brunswick, the big male's mate had laid her full clutch in her tree nest, and sat contentedly on them, watching the patch of sky she could see overhead at the mouth of the cavity. With water lapping at the foot of her tree, she felt very secure.

After the strange incident with her mate and the men in the canoe she did not see him again that spring. His disappearance was, however, only a little earlier than usual, so she thought no more of it. Day after day she fed alone along the channel as the water dropped. One day a pair of bright button eyes in a black-masked face watched her speculatively from the fork of a big old elm.

She dipped and dabbled her way past the elm with its watching raccoon, and then climbed out on the very log where her mate had been caught in the trap. It was clear now, and she rested there preening and arranging her feathers before returning to her nest. When she flew off, the raccoon marked the direction she had taken.

The next day when she returned to feed, the raccoon was sunning himself on a fallen log farther along the channel in the direction she had taken the day before. Again he watched her return to the nest, but she still flew out of sight around a bend. On the third day, as she flew to her nest and disappeared, he set off for her tree.

The female had finished adjusting the eggs to her satisfaction and had settled on them for a long, comfortable stay. At the sound of the first scratch on the base of the tree she became instantly alert. The steady *scratch, crunch, scratch* as the raccoon climbed reached her, and she froze on her nest. For a time there was silence as he explored another branch, but as soon as he returned to the trunk she heard him again.

He came at last to the branch with the cavity, and she braced herself as the relentless noises approached. She could hear the scratches within a few feet of the cavity mouth. Now was the time she would have to act. She flung herself out the entrance as a handlike forepaw reached the lip. The raccoon made a frantic grab for her as she left, and then climbed to the lip of the cavity. Below him lay the eggs.

A few days earlier another canoe had slid silently into the mouth of the channel, and a man with a pair of binoculars around his neck had stepped ashore to make his way quietly along the bank, searching the trees with his glasses. When he came to her tree he had noted the tufts of down at the entrance to the cavity and made a notation on his field map. A week later he came back and climbed the tree. In the nest he found the crushed and eaten shells and even a raccoon dropping full of shell fragments. Raccoon hairs were stuck in the rough walls of the cavity. He recorded one more case of raccoon predation in his field notes and went his way, carefully scanning the trees for the telltale wisps of down hanging from the cavities.

But the female's maternal instincts were still strong, and she turned at once to the selection of a new nest. This time she picked a sheltered moss-lined hollow beneath a bush at the edge of the woods. Again her eggs came one by one, but this time the flow stopped after she had laid six. The down wall around them grew apace, but it was not as dense as at her first nest because her supply was limited. Still, she kept them warm.

She used every trick she knew to hide the nest from any predator, and carefully covered the eggs each time she left them. She had moved about a mile from her unsuccessful first nest and was outside the territory of the raccoon, but now she was vulnerable to the other land predators as well. Her nest was not found until the clutch was within a few days of hatching, when a red fox happened to see her leave.

He trotted over, smelled the nest all over, and then picked up an egg in his mouth and departed. Though he lifted two more the next day, the hen still sat on, unable to detect the dwindling size of her clutch.

On the last day of incubation there were but three eggs left, but that day the fox did not come. The following day the eggs hatched one by one, and the last duckling forced its way from the shell with great vigor. From the first day it was larger and stronger than the others, and it seemed to take its own time in leaving the nest. It was a male, a true possessor of his father's exceptional size and strength. As a rose-breasted grosbeak caroled from an old silver maple nearby, the female led the tiny brood off to the marshes just beginning to rise from the retreating flood.

Several days later the biologist found the vacant nest, and pondered the meaning of the three lone eggshells in it. After he had completed his notes at the end of the nesting season, he counted up the number of nests that had been taken by predators, particularly the raccoon, and recommended predator control in the nesting area for the following year.

When the big male completed his molt at the Bull Pasture Plains, he and his companions returned to Grand Lake and the marshes. He left the strenuous journeying on new wings to younger birds now, and lived a sedate life as befitted his advancing age, restricting his wanderings to the local scene.

He explored the river islands of the St. John where the orange and black of a Baltimore oriole flashed among the trees, and he found the wood duck and teal ponds on Gilbert Island. He joined the gang of blacks in the channel between Gilbert and Ox islands, and he wandered up the

Oromocto to Sunpoke Lake. The Portobello knew him well, and he dropped downriver as far as the concentration area in the great lagoon of Musquash Island. Here a goldfinch roller-coastered beside him as they crossed the water, calling "Ti-dee-di-di" at each downswoop.

Returning to Grand Lake, he flew over the famous Long Pond at Foshay Lake where literally thousands of his kind had been shot. Here he rested and fed beside a clump of withered branches topped with a black tern that was the remains of a last year's blind. The bottom of this pond must contain hundreds of pounds of lead shot, and it was fortunate for him that it sank into the soft mud beyond his reach. In heavily shot areas like this with a hard bottom, the shot lies on the surface and is picked up by the feeding ducks. This can cause sterility and death from lead poisoning.

One day as he was heading for the seclusion of Timber Lake, flying over the Grand Lake marshes under the flat-bottomed cumulus clouds, a young black jumped from a pond and fell in behind. It was a sturdy bird of the year, but already it showed power beyond its age. Another such as he had been in his youth had appeared. The youngster followed him about for several days until it became lost in a group of others. Neither knew they were father and son.

As scarlet and gold touched the maples of the swamps, the old male knew that the hunting season was about to begin, and he adopted his usual fall feeding pattern. He reconnoitered areas that his experience taught him would not be used by hunters and he located feeding areas where he could feel safe. Then he settled down to await the annual holocaust of Opening Day.

The young male had joined a gang of his own age that

were savoring their new power of flight to the full and exploring as widely as possible the wonderful new world it opened to them. His group had flown fifty miles to the west of the river, and one evening they followed some strangers to a small lake beside a railroad station. With no thought of danger the young birds piled in with the others, joining the numbers already there.

They were in a sanctuary that was heavily baited at the banding traps around the water's edge. The precocious youngster was not slow in forcing himself to the forefront where the corn lay thickest, and the next morning found him among a dozen others in the first trap. His size and excellent condition caused comment, and the banders were surprised to see his forked juvenile tail feathers still present, showing he was a bird of the year. He was already large enough to be an adult, and after banding him the biologist cupped his hands and let him stand in them free. He stood for a moment with his head held low, not realizing that he was released, and then with a bound he was off.

Back at Grand Lake the old male successfully evaded the hunters and wended his way south as winter set in. Finally he settled into a marsh below the permanent frost region, and there he spent the winter. There were empty summer cottages all around the rim of his marsh, but these did not bother the wintering ducks. The owners of these houses had, like thousands of other summer cottagers, bought a mosquito-free summer by spraying the marsh with DDT. As they returned to the city, tanned and healthy from their summer at the shore, the waterfowl returned from the North and settled in for the winter.

The old male was standing on his one leg on a mudbar one day, enjoying the last of the sun, when a duck slid in and landed in front of him. His mate of the previous summer swam ashore and walked up to him. They stared at each other for a moment, touched bills, and then she began contendedly preening her feathers. The old male put his head under his wing and went to sleep.

Chapter Fifteen

He was now in his tenth year, well past the normal span of life of his species, but he was still vigorous. As his mate was in the prime of life, she was sought after by the younger males. These the old male chased off as a matter of course, but it seemed less important to him now than ever before. Not only was his ardor weakening with age, but the DDT he had eaten at the Bull Pasture Plains and daily since he arrived on the winter range had settled in his organs. He had not absorbed enough to sterilize him, but it markedly reduced his desire to breed.

The female had missed the DDT poisoning in New Brunswick, but here where they concentrated on the winter range none could miss it, and here the dose was much heavier. Everything they ate had been exposed to the poison, which as the winter passed slowly accumulated in their bodies. A pair of bald eagles wintered there, and they also became contaminated. The local ospreys had been feeding on contaminated food all season, and they too bore a heavy load of the poison. Thus were lives of birds from far and near affected by this method of getting rid of mosquitoes; and as the inevitable clock of the seasons rolled on, the birds got ready to carry the poison many hundreds of miles to places where it was never known before.

Eskimos on the Arctic Islands a thousand miles to the north would acquire their first DDT by eating a bird that had wintered on these marshes, and so also would a great snowy owl sweeping over the barrens of Ungava. All up and down the flyway the effect of the poison was felt as it spread through the food chains of almost all life. Something new had definitely been added to the world of the black ducks, but how long it would last or what effects it would have are still largely unknown. Carrying it, the pair set out for the North that spring.

She followed the edge of the breakup to the Grand Lake marshes of New Brunswick; the male knew well every step of the way. They waited at the goose pasture at Jemseg until the brooks were running and the flood rose into the trees, and then she moved up into the Portobello country. This northwest corner of the waterfowl area was a maze of channels and ponds at this time of year.

The muskrat trappers were out in force as usual. The big male found two wood ducks and a black caught in their traps as he prospected for a territory. Only the black was alive, and its frantic struggles alarmed him enough to abandon any thought of settling nearby. Finally he chose a territory on a backwater that had no connection with the main stream. Trappers would have to walk overland to reach it, which was not worth their while, so they set no traps there and he was undisturbed. The female nested under some bushes on the edge of an opening a quarter of a mile back in the forest above the flood. They settled in to the normal life of the breeding season.

As spring drew to a close the nest remained undetected by any predator, and as incubation ended the male left for his molt. The water level had fallen rapidly, as it was a warm dry season, and the little brook running past the nest into the main stream dried up, leaving the ducklings with a quarter of a mile of rough going through tangled undergrowth before reaching water.

On the day the first egg should have pipped there was no sign of activity, and the female sat on. Two days later the first egg tooth broke through the shell, and she watched as the duckling struggled to free itself. When it finally emerged it meant nothing to her that it was hatched deformed with one of its feet turned inward. She kept the duckling under her wing for another day waiting for the rest of the eggs to hatch. On the third day two more pipped, and this time one duckling had both feet deformed. The other was normal but seemed very weak. It struggled for a long time to get free of the membrane, and when it finally succeeded it lay without moving for so long that she was about to remove it from the nest as dead when it moved slightly.

The living ducklings must be taken to water without delay, so she reluctantly abandoned the nest with seven eggs still unhatched, and started the fateful journey. She did not know that her remaining eggs would never hatch, but she soon found that her two deformed ducklings could travel only at the slowest pace. The weak one had to rest every few yards, so as she led them down the slope and through the tangle she stopped often for them to catch up.

The weak duckling was the first to go. When they were within a hundred yards of the water, it lay down and closed its eyes. She came back to it and coaxed it in every way she could, but it was no use. The weak fluttering heart stopped within a few minutes, and she led on the remaining two.

With thirty yards to go, the inward-turned clubfoot of one of the two survivors became entangled in a mass of dead grass. The duckling struggled with all its might, but its minute strength was not enough. It lay there trapped, waiting to die as she led the last one the remaining distance to the stream. She called and waited, but the answering peep from the tangle grew feebler and finally ceased altogether. She then turned and led the lone clumsily paddling duckling to his first mosquito larvae. Within a week its awkward struggles to keep up had attracted the attention of a pickerel. That day the duck was startled by a swirl behind her, and upon turning found herself alone.

Meanwhile back in the marshes of the mid-Atlantic coast where the blacks wintered, the summer cottagers were streaming out from the cities and the planes were filling up for the next round of mosquito control. The ospreys sailed on their saberlike wings, searching the flats for fish, and their mates returned to their nests in the tops of the tall dead trees.

When their eggs came, many a cottager brought his children to see the great birds sitting on their nests and to watch the graceful flight of their mates. The males, hovering and diving to the water in a thrilling swoop to rise with a silver fish in their talons, never failed to draw gasps of admiration from the onlookers. But as the season progressed the sitting females became more and more restless. The time of hatching came and passed but no sign of life stirred in the eggs. Still the hopeful mothers sat on, but one by one they gave up as the eggs went rotten. That year there were no young ospreys raised there, and the shaggy nests in the tall dead trees were unproductive for the first time since they were built.

The pair of bald eagles that had wintered on the marsh followed the ducks north in the spring, and they too returned to the Portobello swamps of New Brunswick. The nest where the female was hatched was a huge pile of sticks jammed down into the fork of a great elm deep in the flooded forests. Generation after generation of bald eagles had first seen the light of day there, and the young had taken their first plunge into space from the rim of the great nest.

This year the pair returned and inspected the nest when it was still full of snow. As soon as it was empty they began repairing the winter's damage. The muskrat trappers came and went, and the biologist paddled his canoe quietly up to the trunk and sat watching the pair through his binoculars. Their snow-white heads and tails stood out vividly against the blue sky, and he sat still for a long time admiring them.

He recorded the date he first saw them in the spring and each day thereafter, and he noted the day he first found the female sitting. When the time came for the eggs to hatch he spent all day watching from a distance, but he went home disappointed that night as he could see no change in their behavior. Other duties kept him away for three days, but on the fourth he was back. The female was still sitting placidly on the eggs, with the male soaring above and returning at intervals to her. For another week she incubated the eggs. Then she gave up and left the nest. The biologist noted in his fieldbook:

"Female sat for three weeks past the hatching date. No sign of a fledgling, and she left. I checked the nest and found two rotten eggs—too far gone for pesticide analysis. Reproduction NIL for this year."

And so part of the price of a mosquito-free summer was paid far to the north.

As summer drew to a close the big male stayed in the Grand Lake country. Gone was the urge to wander to the far corners of his world. He would sit out in the big lake until it got too rough for his single leg; then he would seek shelter in some secluded bay of the great marshes.

One evening just at dusk he had landed in a slough and was just beginning to feed when the catlike squall of a female wood duck sounded nearby and she landed beside him. Three more followed in quick succession, and as he watched wood ducks began arriving in twos and threes in a steady stream. He had chosen a wood-duck roost where these beautiful birds gather each evening at this time of year. This particular slough seemed no different from any of a half dozen surrounding it, but no wood ducks landed in them; they came only to his slough, and by the time it became quite dark over a hundred had arrived. Their calls and splashing carried a considerable distance across the stillness of the marsh. The biologist listened and entered the location of another wood-duck roost on his map.

The big male was not slow to realize the protective value of this gathering, and each night he joined the throng of wood ducks to feed safely in their midst, amply protected on all sides. One night he was sitting quietly with the woodies when they were silenced by the sudden roar of an engine starting up. It was a very loud engine and it shattered the stillness for several miles around. However, it was not near them, and gradually they resumed feeding.

Hour after hour the engine droned on, and in the distance a powerful light appeared across the marsh. The big male shifted uneasily at these signs of men at this unaccustomed hour, but the wood ducks, being mostly birds of the year, and inexperienced, soon forgot all about it and resumed feeding and chasing each other about. Finally the big male relaxed too, as all seemed normal around him.

As he swam into a lead in the marsh, he suddenly realized that the roar was much louder. A great light, so brilliant he could not look at it, and completely obliterating all behind it, came slowly toward him. Several blue-winged teal and two wood ducks lay directly in the beam, and he sat frozen as it approached them.

Though they swam in little uneasy circles, they seemed hypnotized, and unable to leave the light, and just as it appeared on top of them a long-handled dipnet swept out and picked up one of the teal. There was a muffled flurry in the darkness, and the net flicked out and caught another. One by one the teal and the wood ducks were scooped up and disappeared behind the light. The big male was next. He too sat hypnotized in the blinding beam, unable to hear anything but the never-ending roar that he had listened to for hours.

As the light crept toward him, a voice in the blackness behind said softly, "A big black! Get him!"

At the last minute, when the net had already started for him, he turned away, wrenching his eyes from the glare, and swam swiftly into the grass as the boat drifted past. It took a few seconds for his eyes to clear, and then he saw an airboat, a great light mounted on its bow, and on either side a man holding long dipnets. In the boat was a holding crate full of ducks. He took off at once and flew back to the safety of the open lake.

The boat carried on through the marsh, picking up blinded ducks as it went. When the crate was full it stopped, and the men set to work banding and releasing the ducks. It was a record catch for the region, and the biologists went home satisfied that they had perfected another method of catching ducks for banding that might be of great value in areas where the conventional traps did not work. The big male added another experience to his growing store of knowledge, and never again did he allow the roaring, glaring airboat to approach him as it cruised the marshes at night.

He had already started prospecting for hidden feeding areas where he could drop in during the hunting season and remain secure. He carefully checked each one for signs of man. The first he visited had a new blind erected beside it. The green leaves on the alders rammed into the mud had just started to droop, making it stand out in plain sight amid the surrounding brown marsh grasses. The hopeful hunter had built it in advance so that it would weather before the season opened, but the wise old male never visited that pond again.

Instead he found a wonderfully sheltered pothole beside what appeared to be a deserted track into the marsh. It was much to his liking because no other ducks used it. Here he could slip in unobserved and remain sheltered and comfortable while the others battled the elements on the open lake. The loss of half his power in the water made this necessary, and he availed himself of this safe hideaway whenever it got rough outside.

As the day of the hunters arrived, more and more blinds appeared beside the bays and on the points of the marshes. The big male was perturbed to find that cars now used the track beside his pothole, but he noted shrewdly that none stopped there; they went on past, farther into the marsh. He made note of this, and one evening he deliberately remained in the heavy cover as a car went by twenty yards away. Later a lone man walked out the track. He almost caught sight of the black before he could hide, but he passed on unseeing a few yards away and the big male's confidence grew. At last he had found a secure place where he could hide if men were about when the elements denied him the sanctuary of the lake.

Chapter Sixteen

On the evening before the Great Day, young Jimmy Dawson was too excited to sit still. Tomorrow would be his first
Opening Day, and his father had given him his first honest-
to-goodness duck gun in honor of the occasion.

He and his father had gone out a week before and built
their blind beside the pothole where his father had shot on
Opening Day for years. They noted with satisfaction that
there were no other blinds there. His father had taken
Jimmy up to the gun club and let him shoot several rounds
of skeet with his new gun just to get the feel of it. There
is nothing like the reflexes and the keen eyes of youth;
and after he stopped flinching and settled down, Jimmy

shot sixteen clay targets with his new gun. That evening after his father had inspected his gun and shells; the dog tackle; his boots, coat, and hat; and the anchor lines on the decoys, he pronounced there were only two things left to do now: eat and sleep.

The alarm brought Jimmy out of bed on its first tinkle. They breakfasted long before the first pink appeared in the eastern sky. With a sure touch his father drove along the dim track past the slough in the dark, and Jimmy hung from the window as they passed, searching for ducks.

"Nothing doing there, lad. In all the years we've hunted here, there's never been a duck in there yet."

As they reached the blind and dumped the decoys, the wind from the northeast whistled through the branches.

"At least it's not a bluebird day. There'll be plenty of trading back and forth from the lake in this."

As the light improved, a band of teal wheeled over their decoys with a sound like a splitting sheet, and all around the sound of guns broke the stillness. In a few moments there were ducks in the air wherever they looked, and no one noticed the lone single that flew in high out of gun-shot and dropped silently into the marsh.

By noon Jimmy had shot three ducks, and his father two. They had lost a cripple in the jungle beyond the pond. The morning flight was over, but Jimmy was so tense he could not relax.

"Take it easy for a while now. It won't start again until about four o'clock. Let's have lunch."

Just as the sun was setting, the father completed his limit of six ducks, but Jimmy was still one short when they picked up.

"Dad, I want to jump-shoot that slough back by the car. I'll go on ahead."

"O.K. I'll hump the gear," said his father with a rueful grin.

The boy maneuvered so that the lighted western sky was in front of him; slipping off the safety he started up the edge of the slough.

The big male black had stayed well hidden ːll day in his private pothole. No other ducks attempted to land there, as it was right beside the now well-used track, and he heard men approaching long before they came into sight. As the sun sank in the west the crackle of gunfire grew once more as the ducks came in from the lake at dusk. It was almost dark now, but the western sky was a blaze of orange fire.

Suddenly in the darkness behind him a twig snapped under the unmistakable tread of a man. There was no track there, and someone must have sneaked up on his slough. There was nothing to do now but leave—fast—and he leaped into the air with a great beating of wings to make up for his feeble jump.

The boy's heart nearly stopped with excitement at the sudden commotion before him, but the gun came up with a smooth easy swing. As the big male clawed for altitude, the boy covered him squarely and pressed the trigger. The strong wings folded for the last time. The big male was dead before he hit the water.

"I got one, Dad! And he's a dandy! Bring Tar!"

When they took the duck from the Labrador's mouth, they noticed his single leg with its metal band.

"Look, Dad—he's banded, but there's nothing on it!"

"That's all right. He's a real old-timer, and his band has worn smooth. The people who put them on will know how to bring back his number and get his story. I'll bet it'll be a long one!"

When they reached the car, a gang of blacks wheeled

over their heads. As they banked against the last of the glow with their satin-lined wings shining brightly, a spark of light reflected from the new band on the leg of the big male leading the flock. The son of the old black was coming south from the vast land of angry seas and huge lakes, barren rocks and forested mountains that make up the summer home of the northern black ducks. He would range the flyway as his father had before him, and his race would go on journeying to and fro, with the clock of the seasons setting the pace of their lives.

From Snorri, son of Karlstefni, down to the pilot filling up his plane to spray a marsh, the black ducks have known all the effects of man on the section of the continent in which they live. They saw the last walruses to survive the slaughter on the beaches of Prince Edward Island, and they flew over the eggers and down hunters that doomed the Labrador duck. On their migrations they traveled over most of the tremendous swim of the great auks from the North Atlantic islands to the Carolinas and back each year. They sat watching in the freshwater marshes along the St. Lawrence and the Great Lakes when the passenger pigeons passed in clouds that blotted out the sun.

They heard the barking of the dogs that killed the last sea mink on Campobello Island, and they saw the last great waves of Eskimo curlew in Nova Scotia preparing to take off for South America. The last wolves south of the St. Lawrence howled beside their forest lakes, and the last of the woodland caribou in the Maritimes disappeared while they were molting at the Bull Pasture Plains. Down through the history of the land the black ducks have been spectators of the major events of their world.

Until very recently, when they crossed the St. Lawrence

and the settled areas of southern Canada, heading north in the spring, they were as completely lost to man as if they had migrated to the moon. The vast empty northland was uninhabited, for its sparse Eskimo and Indian population was concentrated at the posts, enjoying a well-earned rest after their arduous winter hunt, and the back country was left to the wildlife for the summer.

But the end of the eons of peace and tranquillity in the northland's summer its fast approaching. Now when the son of the big male flies north, following his mate of the season, he will not disappear into a land untouched by man. Vast cutovers of pulpwood companies stretch along the north shore of the St. Lawrence and follow its tributaries far into the interior. Huge dams are being built to harness the wild rivers for power, and even the taiga of Labrador and Ungava is broken by new mines with their attendant settlements and serving railways. The black ducks nesting in the interior are not immune from man any longer—instead they must be protected from him, even as they are farther south. The days when they could forget men from breakup to fall are over forever.

As they return each year to the only winter home they know, will they consume more and more of the subtle, slow-acting poisons that gradually erode away their desire and ability to breed? Will this be a serious blow to their rate of reproduction, and how long will the residues of these now inescapable poisons last in succeeding generations after the poisons themselves have been superseded by our advancing technology? DDT has already spread to the outermost corners of the earth, including the shores of Antarctica. Birds themselves have carried it to the arctic. Is the end in sight? No one knows the answers to these vital questions.

189

The next generation is already winging north, led by the sleek females who alone know where they are bound. But through no fault of their own, in their loins now lie the seeds of sterility, deformity, and death, and they must pass them on to their young. In the down-lined nests from New England to Ungava, and from Labrador to Hudson Bay, the ducklings will struggle from the membranes of the breaking eggs and follow the duck through the tangle to the nearest water. Will the number with deformed feet and feeble hearts be greater than ever before? Will the number successfully passing the brood stage to fly south in the fall be less than ever before? Some think it will, and that this is already happening. A recent test showed that thirty-six out of thirty-seven clutches of black duck eggs collected in eight states from Maryland to Maine contained an average of fourteen parts per million DDT. Studies with the closely related mallard show that eggs containing only two parts per million DDT have a significantly lower hatching success than those of uncontaminated birds—so what are the black duck's chances?

Those of us who admire him wish him well, but pray that someone will find a way to kill mosquitoes and other troublesome insects—and nothing else—before it is too late.

As I write, the lusty young male rides his new mate's slipstream with narrowed eyes against the blast. He is not concerned with these matters. All he knows is that as the hours of daylight lengthen and the sun lifts higher above the horizon each day, the urge to breed still grows within him. With it also grows the urge to voyage on into the North to faraway places he has never seen. He does not wait for warm weather if there is any open water, and as long as some of it is shallow there is food. His perfectly insulated body protects him from cold, and he is bursting with strength.

He has no inkling yet as to where he is being led, or no real conception of the vastness of the region that is his to explore. He had just reached the Bay of Fundy, and many alternatives are open to him. Only his mate will choose.

Meanwhile, Jimmy Dawson and the thousands like him will stand shivering in the dawn mist, straining their eyes at the dying stars to catch the first outline of the "gold standard" of the eastern wildfowler—the black duck. If help is needed, it will come in large part from these men.